Frontispiece: Hand coloured mezzotint of Toby Fillpot, about 1770

ROYAL DOULTON
Character & Toby Jugs

DESMOND EYLES

ROYAL DOULTON TABLEWARE LIMITED
STOKE-ON-TRENT 1979

Edited by Paul Atterbury & Louise Irvine

Editorial consultant: Richard Dennis

Photography by Prudence Cuming Associates
The author and the publishers would also like to thank
the many other photographers in Great Britain and
North America who have contributed to this book.
Historical photographs used in the introduction are by
courtesy of the American Museum of Natural History,
the British Museum, the City Museum and Art Gallery
Stoke-on-Trent, the Metropolitan Museum of Art
New York, the Museum of the American Indian, the
Museum of London, the University Museum of
Archaeology Cambridge, and the Victoria & Albert
Museum London

Designed by Paul Sharp

Printed in Great Britain by the Westerham Press,
London Road, Westerham, Kent

Bound in Great Britain by R J Ackford Ltd,
Chichester, Sussex

Published and distributed in Great Britain and Europe
by Royal Doulton Tableware Limited, PO Box 100,
London Road, Stoke-on-Trent ST4 7QD

Distributed in the United States of America by
Doulton and Co Inc, 400 Paterson Plank Road,
Carlstadt, New Jersey 07072, USA

Distributed in Canada by Doulton China of Canada
Limited, 10 Carnforth Road, Toronto, Ontario
M4K 2K8, Canada

Distributed in Australia by Doulton Tableware Pty
Limited, PO Box 47, 17–23 Merriwa Street, Gordon,
New South Wales 2072, Australia

© Royal Doulton Tableware Limited, 1979

ISBN 0 906262 01 1

Contents

The Cardinal Character Jug, showing the range of sizes: large, small, miniature and tiny

Acknowledgements

I wish to express my sincere thanks to the Directors and Curators of many museums and art galleries, to the collectors and dealers in Europe and North America and to the many other individuals and organisations who have helped me with the research for this book.

I am particularly indebted to Richard Dennis for acting as a consultant editor for the book, and for giving me access to his information and his photographs which were originally included in his booklet *Doulton Character Jugs*, published in 1976 (now out of print).

I am also grateful to Paul Atterbury for his invaluable help in the production of this book, and for the contribution made by the designer, Paul Sharp, and the printers, Westerham Press Limited.

Finally, I should like to thank the following for their help, and for information so willingly given, in some cases quite recently, and in others many years ago: David Allen, Bob Bentley, Margaret Bentley, Geoffrey Bemrose, William J Carey, Edward R Cross, Walter J Fairhall, Mr & Mrs Robert M Fortune, Captain William Fortune, Reginald Haggar, Leslie Harradine, Max Henk, Eric Hooper, Jocelyn Lukins, Lord Mackintosh of Halifax, Joseph H Mott, Charles J Noke, Cecil J Noke, Mr & Mrs D A Philabaum, E L Pry, and Mr & Mrs J Vitkovics.

DESMOND EYLES

Foreword

Such is the appeal of the Toby Jug (in the shape of a seated or standing figure) and, even more so, of its present-day descendant, the Royal Doulton Character Jug (depicting head and shoulders only) that anyone acquiring one or two – whether by way of gift, purchase or inheritance – is generally fired with the urge to obtain others of the same intriguing *genre*. And so it has come about that there are today thousands of collectors of these fascinating figure jugs in many different lands.

It is primarily for collectors of the Doulton jugs that this book (based in part on *Good Sir Toby*, long since out of print) has been written. In it my aim has been to answer those questions which discussions and correspondence with many collectors and dealers, over the past twenty years, have shown me are most often asked about image jugs in general and about the Royal Doulton productions in particular.

After a brief preliminary discussion of some of their predecessors, the major part of the book is devoted to a detailed record, fully illustrated in colour, of all the Doulton Character and Toby Jugs known to have been made at Burslem since the advent of *John Barleycorn* in 1934 up to the time of going to press. Details of other kindred 'Character Wares', such as musical jugs, tobacco jars, cigarette lighters and ash bowls, are also given as well as of some jugs piloted in market surveys but not put into general production.

The longer list, in alphabetical order, gives the names of the designers, the dates of introduction and, where applicable, of withdrawal of all sizes of all jugs. Contrary to what has sometimes been assumed, where jugs have been made in two, three or four different sizes these were *not* always introduced and/or withdrawn at the same time.

A separate list of discontinued jugs will enable collectors to see at a glance just how long any particular one was in production and to deduce from this its relative rarity.

Who was *Old Charley*? Or *Simon the Cellarer*? Or *Johnny Appleseed*? Questions of this kind are often asked about the origin of some of the characters depicted by the Doulton jugs. For this reason a brief background sketch relating to each one is given.

The twelve tinies: left column, *Cardinal*, *Mr Pickwick*, *Fat Boy*, *John Peel*; centre column, *Paddy*, *Mr Micawber*, *'Arriet*, *Auld Mac*; right column, *Sairey Gamp*, *Sam Weller*, *'Arry*, *Old Charley*

CHAPTER ONE

Characters Worth Knowing

Of the eighteenth-century Toby Jugs by Staffordshire and other British potters only a few thousand are believed to have survived in reasonably good condition. Most of these are now zealously, if not jealously, treasured in private and museum collections. On the relatively rare occasions when genuine Whieldon-type, Wood-type or other Tobies of the period appear in the salerooms (usually when a private collection has, for some reason, to be dispersed) they change hands for large sums, running sometimes not just into hundreds but into thousands of pounds. The scope for collecting such jugs is thus inevitably restricted.

These early Toby Jugs were interesting, if sometimes naive, examples of burgeoning, unsophisticated native craftsmanship. Toby Jugs made last century are somewhat more often seen in antique shops and salerooms but even they, especially those of superior modelling and colouring, are much scarcer now than a decade or two ago. Many of the jugs made in the Victorian era, moreover, are so crude, garish and ill-modelled as hardly to merit collecting except from the standpoint of historical interest. It is very doubtful, indeed, if there are many really desirable old Tobies still reposing in remote country villages waiting to be 'picked up for a song' by some astute collector – but it is not unknown for fakes to be 'planted' in rural inns and 'olde worlde' tea-rooms, or even in hotels and pubs in cities and towns much frequented by tourists.

It may seem at first strange to hear that, despite the scarcity of good earlier specimens, interest in Toby and associated figure jugs is more widespread today than ever before. *Never, in fact, have so many collections been formed – and with such enthusiasm – as during the past forty years.* This apparent paradox is explained by the fact that since 1934 an extensive and fascinating new range of finely-finished Character and Toby Jugs has become available of which an eminent authority on ceramics, Reginald G. Haggar, has said: 'They are of outstanding quality. Their vigorous modelling exhibits a liveliness of observation, shrewd characterisation and humour which worthily continue the tradition of John Voyez and Ralph Wood.'

This is indeed high praise. But the collector, if he compares any of the Royal Doulton jugs – to which the above quotation refers – with the best of an earlier age, will find it well-founded. Skilfully modelled by master-craftsmen and individually hand-painted in harmonious under-glaze colours – so that no two are ever exactly alike – the Doulton jugs have set a standard of ceramic design and finish which is refreshing in these days when, in so many fields, sheer mass-production is the rule. In their wide-ranging choice of subjects, the Doulton designers, finding their inspiration in the rich veins of literature, song, history, folklore and legend, have created, within the age-old tradition of figure jugs, an entirely original *genre* of their own. Compared with earlier jugs in human likeness (the quaint eighteenth-century Tobies not excepted) the Doulton jugs exhibit far greater variety and subtlety in deft characterisations and vividly expressive facial features. Their creators have developed a brilliant flair for epitomising the essence of each character in a single work of art. Unlike the modellers of the old-time Tobies, restricted for the most part to variations on a single theme – *the toper* – so that, after a few years, their jugs tended to become hackneyed, the Doulton designers have been free to allow their fancy to roam far and wide while creating for our delight a whole realm of enchanting and intriguing characters in clay. It is not to be wondered at then that innumerable collectors have found in these Character Jugs, as they are so aptly called, one of the most fascinating by-ways in the realm of ceramics down which to wander and explore.

'Fun and Gains'

People collect pottery and porcelain, just as they collect coins, stamps, antique silver and a host of other things, for many different reasons – among them pleasure, amusement, hoped-for gain, and appreciation of craftsmanship. It is one of the features of the Doulton jugs that they can satisfy *all* these various approaches.

Fun expresses very succinctly one of the great attractions of the Doulton jugs for the appreciative collector. They *are* undoubtedly great fun and can give never-ending pleasure to their owners. They provide excellent talking points and can readily stimulate many an interesting discussion; they can also inspire the collector to delve into the historical facts, legends, myths or other origins which lie behind them and which are merely touched upon briefly in the outline sketches given in the catalogue section.

Since 1934 some 150 different characters have been created, some of them in two or more sizes, making nearly 350 jugs in all. It is the practice to withdraw certain models from time to time and to add others, and there are now 61 characters (153 jugs) in current production. The jugs which have been withdrawn quickly become much sought after collectors' items and tend to increase in value compared with their original cost. Broadly speaking, the shorter the period during which any particular jug was made the rarer it is likely to become. Another factor too must be taken into account concerning jugs introduced before World War Two and withdrawn in 1960 or earlier, as many were. This is that during the war years and for several years afterwards production was on a very limited scale indeed, and then only for export. This accounts for the relative rarity of all twelve 'tinies', and of such jugs as *Mephistopheles*, *Clown*, *Smuts* and several others.

In 1937 the wholesale prices of large-size jugs varied between 18.75p and 25p; those of the small-size between 8.75p and 11.25p. The retail prices would have been higher by 50 per cent or more. In 1947 miniature models were 7.5p and tiny ones 6.25p

On the basis of all past experience, the jugs now in current production are destined in time to become what have aptly been described as 'heirlooms of tomorrow'.

In addition, there are the few jugs which have been christened 'escapees'. These are jugs which were 'piloted' during market surveys but were not subsequently put into production. Such jugs should have been returned to the factory either to be destroyed or to be kept for inclusion in some future survey. Occasionally, in the past, despite all precautions, a few of these jugs have got into other hands and they are naturally extremely rare; among those which have been authenticated are *Hatless Drake*, *Buffalo Bill* and *The Maori*.

Unfortunately some others said to have been of Doulton manufacture have proved to be fakes – and not very clever ones at that. Collectors of some experience are not likely to be deceived by this kind of fake but if there is the slightest doubt they would be well advised to consult a reputable dealer or obtain high-quality colour photographs (three views, including the base) and send these to Royal Doulton for their opinion.

Some of the regular Doulton jugs have occasionally been imitated, but once the collector has become familiar with the genuine jugs he is not likely to be deceived. The difference in modelling, colour and finish is so great as to be at once apparent.

The collector who obtains most satisfaction from his hobby is fired primarily by the delights and excitements of the quest; the question of gains usually is a secondary consideration. The question of the cost of collecting cannot, however, be ignored, especially in these days of world-wide inflation. The collector of the Doulton jugs, in addition to the fun to be gained, has the satisfaction of knowing that all the evidence of the past goes to show that they may be a very worthwhile investment.

Scent bottle in the form of a girl, Eastern
Greek, c540 BC

Red figure drinking cup, modelled on one side as a
satyr and on the other as a woman, Greek, c500 BC

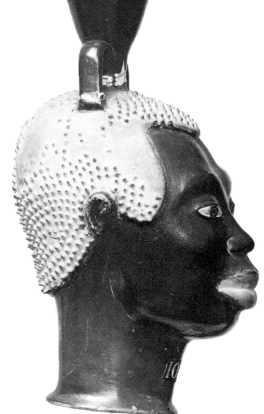

Vase in the form of a negro's head, Greek, c500 BC

Face jug from Lincoln with inscription
Do Mercurio, Roman

CHAPTER TWO

Toby Fillpot

The distinct type of jug in the shape of a seated or standing figure, and now known as the Toby Jug, was almost certainly the creation of some unknown eighteenth-century Staffordshire potter. Quaint, rumbustious and racy, besides forming a fit container for heady beverages, it reflected the spirit of a convivial and vigorous age. Within a few years of its first appearance it had become one of the most popular jugs ever made in human likeness. Its fame soon spread from England to North America and other parts of the world.

Toby's Ancient Ancestry

Though entirely original in conception, Toby was the descendant of a long line of jugs in human form fashioned by potters in earlier times. From the dawn of history, indeed long before man began to record his experiences and ideas in writing, potters have made images of living beings. Some probably played a part in religious rituals or sorcery; others, one can well believe from their appearance, were created out of a sheer sense of fun. Laughter is a faculty which distinguishes man from all other creatures; the *Jolly Potters* who have given their name to many an English tavern assuredly had their counterparts in the Ancient World.

Ancient Greece provides a wealth of examples of jugs, cups, perfume pots and wine vessels made in the likeness of human beings, satyrs, sphinxes and other mythical creatures. Arthur Lane, in his book *Greek Pottery*, remarks that in each generation of Athenian potters there was at least one 'fun-specialist'. Etruscan, Danubian and Roman potters also made similar image-wares; an unusual Roman face-urn from Lincoln with an inscription *DO MERCURIO* ('I give this to Mercury') is illustrated. It is interesting to find that a Roman potter in Staffordshire was also making face-urns, some fifteen hundred years before Toby made his appearance.

A prolific output of hand-moulded image and portrait jugs came from Peruvian and other South American potters. They range from the most primitive types to

Left: Peruvian water bottles of the Mochica period, 1st century AD

Right: North American jar representing a human head, found in Mississippi County, Arkansas

Cup in the form of a friar, early 15th century

exquisitely modelled naturalistic portraits. In North America too, many examples of anthropomorphic pots have been discovered.

Numerous medieval English jugs and pitchers moulded in human shape, or with ornamentation in the form of grotesque human masks, have been found. An interesting example is a fifteenth-century drinking cup which, when turned upside down, reveals a friar. Another notable specimen, depicting a crowned and bearded head, is believed to commemorate Edward II.

Although the piper illustrated is not in the form of a jug it has certain affinities with the later Tobies. In this and other wares of the medieval potter one glimpses the same spirit of fun and good-natured leg-pulling that is expressed in early English literature, especially in the works of Geoffrey Chaucer. English pottery was in its beginnings an essentially rustic craft. It is not surprising then that the strong vein of peasant humour, portrayed so well in some of Chaucer's characters and in Shakespeare's mechanicals, should have found expression in the earthenware fuddling cups, toad mugs, puzzle jugs, posset pots and similar wares which preceded the creation of Toby Fillpot himself.

'Greybeards' or 'Longbeards' are names given to a distinctive type of vessel made by Rhineland potters from the fifteenth century onwards. These German stoneware jugs portrayed on the necks bearded human faces. They later became popularly known as 'bellarmines' – a name said to have been give them by Protestant potters to ridicule the Italian theologian, Cardinal Bellarmine (1542–1621) who was a notorious opponent of the reformed religion. Similar jugs were made in Fulham and Lambeth in England. It is possible that the expression 'ugly mug' may have been derived from the bellarmine.

In Staffordshire, in the early eighteenth century some droll and now very rare

Green glazed earthenware bust of a piper, 14th or 15th century

Buff earthenware jug thought to represent King Edward II, 14th century

Earthenware jug, 14th century

Earthenware pitcher found at Cambridge, 14th century

Buff earthenware jug, late 13th century

Slip decorated earthenware jug, 17th or early 18th century

Two German salt-glazed stoneware Bellarmines, 17th century

Astbury/Whieldon
musician figures, c1745

small earthenware figures and figure jugs were made, depicting midshipmen, soldiers, musicians and other characters of the period c.1730–60. They are generically known as 'Astbury-type' wares but were probably made by several different potters in and around Stoke. They appear to have been the immediate forerunners of the Toby Jug; some of them have tri-corn hats pinched out in the front to facilitate pouring and the hollow seated figures are holding, jugs, pipes and beakers. They are rather crudely modelled and glazed, with black blobs for eyes and buttons, but they show us that the Staffordshire potter was learning to depict the drolleries and humour of everyday life in rural England, remote as yet from the continental influences so evident in the Chelsea and Bow china figures.

And then suddenly, out of the blue – or perhaps one should say straight out of some Staffordshire tavern, an entirely new creation appeared on the scene – a figure jug depicting plain-faced, squat-bodied Toby Fillpot, excelling in modelling and colouring anything of the kind previously seen in Staffordshire.

Toby Fillpot

The name *Toby* was used originally to describe those jugs which were in the form of a *seated* male figure in a tri-corn hat, holding a beer jug on his knee and sometimes a pipe or glass in his hand. The hat was so fashioned that each corner formed a convenient spout. Some of the early Tobies had heavy coarse features and lank hair but rather more genial-looking ones soon appeared, depicting various characters. Toby was attired in typical costume of the period – full-length coat with low-set pockets, broad waistcoat, cravat, knee breeches, stockings and buckled shoes. Some jugs bore the owner's name or an apt – but sometimes incorrectly spelt – inscription such as 'It's all out, then fill agian'. An interesting feature of the early jugs is the hollow cap or crown which was fitted into the top to complete the hat, and which could be used as a cup. Many have now been lost.

Before long several variations were introduced, including standing figures and female figures, but 'Toby' persisted as a generic description. Why this name – a familiar form of Tobias – was given to these jugs remains a matter of conjecture.

Early Staffordshire Toby jugs, c1760

Staffordshire Toby figure, in Ralph Wood style, c1770

Enoch Wood style Toby jug, c1800

Early Wood-type musician jug, c1770

The bestowal of personal names and nicknames on inanimate objects is a general folk tendency; they have often been given to vessels of different kinds – such as jorum, jeroboam, demijohn, puncheon, bellarmine, black jack and billy. The word 'toper', meaning one who imbibes alcohol too freely, was in common use long before the Toby Jug was created, as was the expression 'Tope', probably derived from the French and meaning 'I pledge you'. Bearing in mind the native genius for coining apt nicknames – as witness our Elizabethan and Restoration playwrights – it is not difficult to imagine how *Toby Fillpot* or *Toby Philpot* came into existence.

The name Toby was exuberantly associated with conviviality by Shakespeare in the person of that lovable rascal, Sir Toby Belch, in the comedy *Twelfth Night*. Sir Toby was 'sure care's an enemy to life', loved cakes and ale, and had a novel theory of the relativity of time which he expressed in the words: 'Not to be a-bed after midnight is to be up betimes.' It has been suggested that he inspired the original Toby Jug but this seems unlikely. There is little if any resemblance between the stolid-looking early Tobies (the 'ordinary models' as they are called) in their eighteenth-century costume and the caper-cutting reveller who bestrode the Elizabethan stage at a much earlier date.

Another candidate sometimes put forward as the inspirer is 'My Uncle Toby', a central figure in Laurence Sterne's ribald, witty and bizarre novel *Tristram Shandy*. This was published in 1760, not long before the ordinary model made its

18

Female Toby in Enoch Wood style, c1790

Enoch Wood style Toby figure, c1810

debut, but on the other hand, Uncle Toby, a popular subject for eighteenth-century artists and sculptors, was almost invariably depicted in a soldier's uniform, with a full-bottomed Ramilles wig, and with one foot swathed in bandages because of his gout.

'The Brown Jug'

The late Richard Aldington, novelist, poet and biographer, pointed out that the name Toby Fillpot occurred – probably for the first time *in print* – in a song, *The Brown Jug*, published in 1761 in a volume of *Original Poems and Translations* by the Reverend Francis Fawkes; it is likely that it had been in conversational use before that date. Fawkes, a Yorkshire man by birth, was rector of Orpington in Kent, and judging by some of his poems would have made a good model for the jovial Doulton Character Jug of *Parson Brown*. Here is an extract from one of them:

> 'My friends with generous liquor I regale,
> Good port, old hock, or, if they like it ale;
> But if of richer wine you choose a quart
> Why, bring and drink it here, with all my heart!'

The Brown Jug (also known as *The Metamorphosis* or *Toby Reduc'd*) was Fawkes' clever and very free translation of a Latin poem by the sixteenth-century Italian humanist physician, Geronimo Amalteo, telling the story of one Gubertus

Noricus, a great inbiber of choice Falernian wines. Noricus was metamorphosed by Fawkes into the very English toper, Toby Fillpot, and the Falernian into good old English stingo.

The song, which was soon set to rousing, rollicking music and remained popular for at least a century, goes as follows:

> Dear Tom, this brown jug that now foams with mild ale,
> (In which I will drink to sweet Nan of the Vale)
> Was once Toby Fillpot, a thirsty old soul,
> As e'er drank a bottle, or fathom'd a bowl;
> In boosing about 'twas his praise to excell,
> And among jolly topers he bore off the bell.
>
> It chanc'd as in dog-days he sat at his ease
> In his flow'r-woven arbour as gay as you please,
> With a friend and a pipe puffing sorrows away,
> And with honest old stingo was soaking his clay,
> His breath-doors of life on a sudden were shut,
> And he died full as big as a Dorchester butt.
>
> His body, when long in the ground it had lain,
> And time into clay had resolv'd it again,
> A potter found out in its covert so smug,
> And with part of fat Toby he form'd this brown jug,
> Now sacred to friendship, and mirth, and mild ale,
> So here's to my lovely sweet Nan of the Vale.

Within a few years, these verses appeared under a mezzotint featuring a caricature of an enormously fat old toper with a foaming jug in one hand and clay pipe in the other. He is dressed in much the same style as that adopted for the early Toby Jugs. This was the first of several prints in the same vein; the one reproduced as the frontispiece was published about 1770 by Bowles and Carver.

It may be that the figure depicted in one of these prints inspired some Staffordshire potter to mould the first Toby Jug. On the other hand, whoever it was may well have found a living model sitting contentedly in some local tavern, as suggested in Gordon Nicoll's imaginary scene illustrated opposite. A toper after the example of the Staffordshire inn-keeper, Boniface, depicted in George Farquhar's *The Beaux Stratagem*, would have served very well. He had in his cellar 'ten tun of the best ale in Staffordshire . . . smooth as oil, sweet as milk, clear as amber, and strong as brandy' and had himself 'fed purely upon ale' which served him as both meat and drink for eight-and-fifty years, thus accounting for his considerable bulk. This play by Farquhar was produced several times in the early eighteenth century and could well have been seen by Ralph Wood, Aaron Wood, John Voyez or some other modeller of the time.

Toby has been associated also with a Yorkshire tippler, Paul Parnell, who according to the *Gentleman's Magazine* of 1810 is stated to have drunk during his lifetime £2,000 worth of Yorkshire stingo 'of the home brewed best quality' at two pence per silver pint cupful. The same journal says Parnell was 'the *bon vivant*' whom O'Keefe celebrated in more than one of his Bacchanalian songs, under the appellation of Toby Philpot. (O'Keefe was the author of *The Poor Soldier*, a popular ballad opera first presented in 1783). Another often-quoted story tells of a second notorious Yorkshire toper, Henry Elwes, nicknamed Toby Fillpot, who, it is said, drank 2,000 gallons of strong ale from a brown jug before he died in 1761.

But it is just as likely that these were but two of many heavy drinkers jocularly known by the same nickname and there is no proof whatever that they had anything to do with the origins of the Toby Jug. All we can say is that, where its origins are concerned, many theories have been advanced but, as yet, no certain answer.

'Put Toby this Way'

Besides being displayed in the chimney-corners or on window-sills of farmhouses and cottages, many Toby Jugs were formerly used in taverns, hostelries and homes as drinking vessels and for replenishing tankards, mugs and glasses with ale and beer. Before tea, coffee and cocoa became popular, ale had long been the national drink and even children drank 'very small beer'.

The use of Toby Jugs for drinking from continued well into the nineteenth century and this probably explains why out of the fairly large numbers believed to have been made by numerous potters in Staffordshire, Yorkshire, Scotland and other places only a small proportion has survived in good condition.

In Thomas Hughes' *Tom Brown's Schooldays*, published in 1857, we find the phrase 'pouring out his ale from a Toby Philpot Jug'. Even better known is the passage in Charles Dickens' *Barnaby Rudge* where Gabriel Vardon asks his daughter, Dolly, 'to put Toby this way'. Gabriel's Toby was a 'goodly jug of well-browned clay, fashioned into the form of an old gentleman . . . atop of whose bald head was a fine white froth, answering to his wig, indicative beyond dispute, of sparkling home-brewed ale'.

Painting by Gordon Nicoll of the Staffordshire Figure Makers, from his sequence, *Pottery Through the Ages*

Early Wood-type Toby jug, c1770

Left: Earthenware Silenus jug, Staffordshire, c1780

Right: Earthenware Fair Hebe jug, modelled by Voyez and probably made at the Wood factory, c1790

CHAPTER THREE

Tobies and Their Makers

It is not known by whom, or exactly when, the first Toby Jug was made. It probably made its appearance between 1760 and 1770. Some authors give a date as early as 1750 but there is no conclusive evidence for this. It has to be borne in mind when comparing various examples that the most naive and primitive in style are not necessarily the earliest in date; they may have been made by potters whose methods of modelling and colouring were less advanced than those of the better craftsmen they were seeking to emulate.

In 1750 there were scores of small thatched pot-works in that district of North Staffordshire which is now familiarly known all over the world as 'The Potteries'. The potters' assistants seem, by and large, to have been a happy-go-lucky set of fellows, many of whom migrated from one pot-works to another as the spirit moved them. It was not unusual for pot-works to be bought and sold complete with models and stock, and one potter often helped another during rush periods by making wares for him. Most of the potteries were little more than thatched huts; it is said that Thomas and John Wedgwood built the first works that was not thatched in 1750.

Among the famous names associated with the early development of Staffordshire figures and Toby Jugs, the following are outstanding:

John Astbury	(c.1678–1743)
Thomas Whieldon	(c.1719–95)
Ralph Wood I	(1715–72)
Aaron Wood	(1717–85)
Josiah Wedgwood	(1730–95)
Ralph Wood II	(1748–95)
Enoch Wood	(1759–1840)

Even among this small group there were many inter-relationships, both of a family and a business nature. Ralph Wood I and Whieldon had both been apprenticed to John Astbury, who is generally believed to have been the first of the great Staffordshire figure makers. Whieldon had the young Josiah Wedgwood as a partner from 1754 to 1759. Ralph Wood I was connected by marriage with the Wedgwood family and rented his first pot-works from Thomas and John Wedgwood. Aaron Wood, the famous block-cutter or mould-maker, a brother of Ralph I, had been an apprentice of Whieldon and later became his foreman; afterwards, according to his son, Enoch, he sold his services as a 'modeller to all potters in Staffordshire'. (He has, for this reason, been described as the 'back-room boy' of the early English pottery industry.) Enoch Wood was for a time apprenticed to Wedgwood, and afterwards to Humphry Palmer of Hanley.

The earliest Toby Jugs were not marked with the maker's name; there are no written records concerning them; and one potter often copied the designs of another. In view of these facts and the involved relationships already mentioned, it is impossible to unravel the exact truth as to Toby's 'onlie begetter'. The picture is further complicated by the enigmatic figure of the peripatetic Frenchman, John Voyez, who – both as a modeller and a toper – assuredly has a place in the story.

Voyez was a man of many accomplishments – jeweller, carver, metalworker, glassworker and pottery modeller. Josiah Wedgwood, with high hopes of gaining an advantage over his competitors, hired him as a modeller in 1768 and

Left: American Toby jug, made at the Bennington factory in about 1850

Right: Page from a catalogue published by Kent & Co, Burslem in 1955, showing Toby wares still in production

entertained him in his own home until a new house could be made ready for him 'in the Grandee part of the City of Burslem'. But it was not long before Voyez fell into disgrace. The story goes that Wedgwood found him one day modelling a nude woman (some say she was the daughter of Wedgwood's coachman) and, as if this were not bad enough, both sculptor and model were visibly under the influence of porter – a brew to which Voyez was much addicted. Wedgwood told Voyez he should eschew alcohol and go the classics for his models; Voyez retorted that an artist should go to Nature and not to Italian drawings!

Whatever the truth may have been, Voyez was sentenced at Stafford Assizes to be whipped with a 'cat-o'-nine tails', and to spend three months in prison. When he came out, Wedgwood offered to pay him his full term of three years on condition that he left the country and did not work for his rivals. Voyez, of whom Wedgwood himself had said he could work 'more effectually than all the potters in the country put together', flatly refused; he continued, in fact, to work in Staffordshire for other potters, including Ralph Wood and Humphry Palmer. Palmer was a formidable and by no means undistinguished rival whom Wedgwood positively detested and against whom he constantly inveighed as a blatant plagiarist: Voyez could probably have conceived no more effective way of annoying his former patron.

There are contradictory opinions among collectors and museum experts as to what part, if any, Voyez played in the modelling of Toby Jugs from the Wood factory. Some attribute considerable influence to him; others hardly any. It is known that for a time Ralph Wood and Voyez shared lodgings in Burslem and Voyez' signature is found on a few pieces made at the Wood factory, including some jugs in the form of a tree trunk, with figures of bird-nesters around it and a scroll panel inscribed 'Fair Hebe'. As regards the Toby Jugs we are in a realm of conjecture rather than facts.

Whieldon and the Woods

Certain unmarked Toby Jugs are described as Whieldon-type. There is no sure evidence that Thomas Whieldon made any of these. There are, however, some similarities between the style of glazing and colouring of a number of Toby Jugs and that of certain figures whose origin can be ascribed more confidently to Whieldon's thatched pot-works at Fenton Low.

With the Wood family we are, for the first time in the story of the Toby Jug, on surer ground. Ralph Wood I (or Ralph Wood the Elder) and his son, Ralph Wood II, both made figures and Toby Jugs in their factory in Burslem, the mother-town of the Staffordshire potteries. They were among the first English potters to use their names or a rebus-mark of trees (i.e. wood) to identify some of their wares. Aaron Wood, as already mentioned, worked for a time for Whieldon. The preparation of the plaster moulds from the original model called for great exactitude and painstaking craftsmanship and block-makers – who often combined the functions of designers, modellers and mould-makers – were in great demand. Aaron was much esteemed throughout the Potteries as a cheerful, jolly fellow. According to his son, Enoch, 'although he never had sworn, taken snuff or sung in his life' he was considered 'the most lively, pleasant and merriest man in the country'. Two years younger than Whieldon, two years older than his brother, Ralph I, perhaps he was the creator of Toby? One can only speculate.

Enoch Wood, Aaron's son, produced many figures and figure jugs from existing models, besides introducing several new models, including standing Tobies. By the end of the eighteenth century and the early part of the next, there were many other makers of Toby Jugs of good, bad and indifferent quality not only in Staffordshire but in Yorkshire, Derbyshire, Bristol, Liverpool, Newcastle-on-Tyne, Sunderland and Scotland. The art of making these jugs was introduced also into the United States of America, probably by potters from Stoke who emigrated there in the late eighteenth century.

A Goodly Company

Whoever his originator may have been, it was not long before Toby Fillpot was joined by a number of congenial cronies but no matter who the real or fictitious new subjects might be, or of which sex, the general description *Toby* was retained in popular usage. Among the many more specific names given to the newcomers – sometimes by the makers, sometimes by collectors – are *The Thin Man, The Hearty Good Fellow, The Night-Watchman, The Man on a Barrel, The Sailor, The Planter, The Convict, The Parson*. Best known of the female Tobies is *Martha Gunn*, a bathing attendant at Brighton, Sussex, who is reputed to have taught George IV, when he was Prince of Wales, to swim.

CHAPTER FOUR

Doulton Lambeth Figure Jugs

During most of the nineteenth century and the early part of this there was, with few exceptions, a sad decline in the standard of modelling and painting of Toby Jugs; the general tendency was to produce these in quantity as quickly as possible and to disregard quality. Like so many of the Staffordshire figures of the same period, the jugs were often crudely shaped, with no pretence to good modelling, garishly coloured, poorly glazed and finished. Many have 'crazed' badly, i.e. developed cracks in the glaze, due to faulty firing. The on-glaze enamel colours are often cold and hard, and are inclined to flake off easily.

An interesting development of the same period, on the other hand, was a revival of the figure jug, showing a head or head and shoulders only, inspired perhaps by the Ancient Greek satyr and other face-jugs, of which many were coming to light as a result of excavations by archaeologists. This revival led on eventually to what is now known as the Character Jug – an entirely new treatment and modern metamorphosis of a very ancient expression of the potter's art, craft and humour.

Left: Two salt-glazed stoneware Silenus jugs, probably Fulham, late 18th century

Right: Early 19th century salt-glazed stoneware face jugs, probably Lambeth

Some of the best-modelled and sometimes droll and amusing English figure jugs, dating back to the late eighteenth century, were made in brown salt-glaze stoneware by several potters in Fulham, Mortlake, Lambeth and the Midlands. Stoneware is a strong vitrified ceramic material; the salt-glaze variety is made by inserting salt (sodium chloride) into the kiln when the temperature reaches some 1,250° centigrade, whereupon the sodium constituent combines with elements in the clay to form a thin but exceptionally hard transparent glaze. The stoneware figure jugs ranged from tiny fascinating 'gin nip' measures for taverns, in the likenesses of Robert Peel, Wellington, Napoleon and other well-known personages, to large flattened jugs representing John Barleycorn crushed between two millstones, as described in Robert Burns' well-known ballad.

To mark the passing of the first Reform Bill in 1832 (which abolished some of the worst abuses of the methods then in vogue at Parliamentary Elections and whetted the Liberal appetite for more reforms) cordial and spirit flasks and large bottles were made at Lambeth and Denby in large quantities, though they are surprisingly scarce today. The necks of these containers portrayed King William

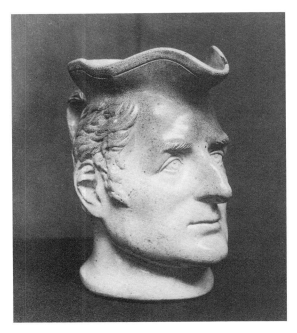

Left: Early 19th century Lambeth salt-glazed stoneware jug depicting the Duke of Wellington

Right: Early 19th century Lambeth salt-glazed stoneware jug depicting Napoleon

IV, the Lords Grey, Brougham and Russell, and others associated with the Bill. John Doulton, the founder of the Royal Doulton Potteries and twenty of his men made many thousands of these 'Reform Bottles' and 'Reform Flasks' as they were called. Most of them bore slogans such as 'The Second Magna Carta', 'The People's Rights', 'Reform Cordial', and 'The True Spirit of Reform'.

John Doulton

John Doulton (1793–1873) had been apprenticed for seven years as a thrower (one who shapes pots by hand on a revolving wheel) to a descendant of the famous John Dwight – often called 'the father of English pottery' – at the Fulham Works which Dwight had founded in the seventeenth century. Fulham was then still a small Thames-side village a few miles up-river from Westminster.

In 1815, Doulton invested his live-savings of £100 in a one-third partnership in an obscure little stoneware pot-house in Vauxhall Walk, Lambeth – one of several such in the neighbourhood. This humble enterprise, was destined to

Two early 19th century salt-glazed stoneware spirit flasks

Left: Late 18th century Fulham salt-glazed stoneware Hunting Jug, showing a Hogarthian scene in relief

Right: Early 19th century Lambeth or Fulham salt-glazed stoneware Hunting Jug

expand through the years and decades into what is now the largest pottery group in the world, bearing the proud name of Royal Doulton. The story of the evolution of the Lambeth Pottery is told in detail in *The Doulton Lambeth Wares* (Desmond Eyles, Hutchinson, 1975).

Among Doulton's earliest productions were salt-glaze stoneware Toby Jugs (also known as 'Hunting Jugs') of a traditional type that had been made in Fulham and Lambeth for many decades. It was while at the Fulham Pottery that John Doulton had learned to make them and he continued to produce them at Lambeth. Unlike the Whieldon, Wood and other Staffordshire Tobies, these were of a conventional jug shape but were ornamented with moulded reliefs in a lighter coloured clay, depicting not only Toby Fillpot and other topers with foaming tankards but a medley of other motifs which, according to the space available and the potter's fancy, might include huntsmen and hounds, foxes, stags and hares, windmills, trees and cottages, and – rather more rarely – Hogarthian scenes and Saint George and the Dragon. These reliefs were made in separate small moulds and then fixed to the surface of the jug by means of liquid clay.

Other early Doulton products included a variety of figure flasks, jugs and mugs in the likenesses of Nelson, Napoleon, Wellington, Queen Caroline, King William IV, Queen Victoria and other Royalties. Those depicting Admiral Lord Nelson are superbly modelled and are considered by some connoisseurs to be among the finest examples of ceramic sculpture produced in England since the time of Dwight.

The production of the relief-figured type of Toby ware continued on an ever diminishing scale from c.1815 up to 1956 when the Lambeth Works closed. Those with the Doulton & Watts mark and the Doulton Lambeth mark (without the word England) are the rarest. The later examples are not at all scarce. Some seated Tobies, more in the Wood style but in plain brown salt-glaze stoneware, were made between about 1910 and 1930 on a small scale, these included some miniatures about $2\frac{3}{4}$ inches (7 cm) high. In 1925 several other seated Tobies, a few plain brown but mostly coloured, were added to the range. These were designed by Harry Simon who also introduced other items incorporating quaint toper figures – covered ash-pots and ink-pots; match-stands and ash-trays; candlesticks and tobacco jars; cork-stoppered flagons, beakers and teapots. These are all rare today for they were made for only about five years in limited quantities. Though partly inspired by earlier Tobies, the coloured ones especially are very distinctive with their unusually vivid colouring. The method of colouring was similar to that used for coloured Parian wares of the late nineteenth century. The separate sections of the plaster moulds were coated with slip (liquid clay of cream-like consistency) of the required colour and then assembled; uncoloured slip for the body was next poured into the mould, whereupon the two kinds of slip united by adhesion, without intermingling.

Simeon first studied modelling and sculpture at the Huddersfield School of Art, where he won a scholarship to what is now the Royal College of Art at South Kensington. He came to Doulton of Lambeth in 1896, where he remained for

Doulton & Watts salt-glazed stoneware figure jug depicting Nelson, c1830

Page from a Doulton catalogue of about 1925, showing the range of Toby wares designed by Harry Simeon

Three salt-glazed stoneware face jugs modelled by the Martin Brothers, c1890–1910

forty years. He was a gifted, versatile artist, whose wide range of designs included large wall plaques, the rare and brightly coloured 'Persian Ware', leopard-skin stoneware and terracotta gardern ornaments, besides the Toby Ware already referred to. According to J. H. Mott, Art Director of the Lambeth Studios, it was during one of his visits to Lambeth that Charles Noke first conceived the idea of a Staffordshire figure jug revival, after seeing the interesting achievements in this field by Simeon and two other Lambeth designers, Mark V. Marshall and Leslie Harradine.

The quaint stoneware face-jugs, full of whimsical fancy, made by Mark V. Marshall, much admired designer of Doulton Lambeth Wares, and by the remarkable Martin Brothers of Southall are among the most unusual examples of

this particular *genre* in the late nineteenth and early twentieth centuries. Marshall, before joining the Art Department at the Doulton Lambeth Pottery, about 1879, had been a stone-carver working on Victorian Gothic Revival churches. He had also spent some time assisting the Martin Brothers and it was doubtless they who stimulated his taste for the impish and grotesque.

A. Leslie Harradine

One of the earliest, possibly the earliest, Harradine figure-flask, is that of Doctor Samuel Johnson, designed in 1909 for the bicentenary of the famous lexicographer's birth; this was followed about three years later by a series of other flasks, somewhat in the style of the 1832 Reform Flasks but better-finished, portraying several of the best-known political figures of the period – Lloyd George, Asquith, Chamberlain, John Burns, Haldane and Balfour. Harradine also designed several studies of popular Dickens characters in the form of both figures and jugs. These were forerunners of the Staffordshire figure and figure jug revivals by Doulton of Burslem in both of which he played an important role.

Arthur L. Harradine (known always to his friends and colleagues by his second name, Leslie) was born in 1887. He joined Doulton of Lambeth in 1902 as an apprentice modeller and designer, working at different times under three of the

Salt-glazed stoneware spirit flask depicting Dr Johnson, modelled at Lambeth by Leslie Harradine, 1909

Set of six salt-glazed stoneware spirit flasks modelled at Lambeth by Leslie Harradine, c1909 and depicting famous politicians, left to right: Balfour, Haldane, Burns, Asquith, Lloyd George and Chamberlain

most distinguished Lambeth designers – George Tinworth, Mark V. Marshall and John Broad. In 1902 he also entered the Camberwell School of Art as a part-time student under the well-known sculptor, Albert Toft. After the First World War he worked as a freelance designer and artist, mainly for Doulton of Burslem. Many of the most famous Royal Doulton figures were his creations, as were several of the early Character Jugs, featuring in his inimitable way well-known Dickens characters.

Salt-glazed stoneware Character Jug of a highwayman, modelled at Lambeth by Leslie Harradine, c1912

White stoneware jug depicting Mr Pecksniff, modelled by Leslie Harradine, c1912

CHAPTER FIVE

The Burslem Toby and Character Jugs

In the early 1930s, Charles J. Noke, Art Director of the Royal Doulton Potteries, Burslem – whose *flambé*, 'Sung', 'Chang', 'Titanian', 'Chinese Jade' and 'Crystalline' wares, among many other contributions to the ceramic art, had brought him world-wide fame – conceived the idea not only of a twentieth-century revival of the earlier Staffordshire Toby Jug tradition but also of an entirely new approach to the design of what up to then were known usually as face-jugs. These he envisaged in a much more colourful style and in a far more varied range than the few which had been made on a restricted scale at Lambeth. What he had in mind was a series of original character studies in English song, literature, legend and history, designed to appeal to his and future generations just as the original Toby Jugs did to our ancestors, and still do to us today.

Charles Noke was born in Worcester in 1858 in the very atmosphere of pottery. His birthplace was within a short distance of the famous china factory in that city. His father, an antique dealer and connoisseur, had one of the largest collections in the Midlands of English and foreign pottery and porcelain so that from his earliest years Charles was able to absorb a great deal of knowledge about the ceramic art and particularly about Chelsea, Bow, Derby, Sèvres and Meissen figures. These came to have a great fascination for the boy who, as a special privilege, was sometimes allowed to handle them. It is said that he was constantly asking his father questions about these and their designers and, indeed, about the many other wares which passed in and out of the shop in the course of trade.

Noke's father had friends and acquaintances among the directors and staff of the Worcester Royal Porcelain Company which in 1862 succeeded variously-titled earlier china factories that had been active in Worcester since about 1751. Among them was the gifted modeller, James Hadley. Permission was given for Charles to visit the china-works sometimes during his holidays and the lad, who became well known there, delighted in going from one workshop and studio to another, asking the occasional pertinent question, and imbibing much information about the making and designing of china. He was especially fascinated by the modellers' work and the way in which their original conceptions were transformed into glistening, colourful porcelain. He was at times allowed to take some modelling clay home with him, and from this he began to shape small animal models and human figures. Much to his joy, Hadley said these showed promise. It is hardly surprising that at the age of sixteen he began work in the Worcester factory as an apprentice modeller and designer; at the same time he started on a long course of theoretical and practical studies at the Worcester School of Design. He stayed with Royal Worcester for some sixteen years until 1889 when he moved to Doulton at Burslem as their Chief Modeller.

The first important fruits of his activities there were seen at the Chicago Exhibition of 1893 in many of the tablewares and ornamental wares, most notably in a series of large vases modelled by Noke in a general Renaissance style and richly painted to his suggestions by Labarre, Mitchell, Wilson, Piper and other ceramic artists. It was in the modelling of the figures incorporated in these vases, as well as as in some table-centrepieces, lamps and candelabras, that Noke's gifts in this field were first publicly revealed and acclaimed. One American commentator wrote that some of his work 'suggested rather the atelier of the sculptor and painter than the workshop of a pottery . . . elevated as it is to the highest pinnacle of art'. His 'Columbus Vase', standing nearly six feet high and surmounted by a bold and picturesque figure of the great seafarer, was described by the *Staffordshire Sentinel* as 'a triumph of pottery . . . the whole composition a marvel and a delight'.

Noke had had the general idea of the Character Jugs in his mind for many years but his preoccupations with the *flambé* and other wares already mentioned and, above all, with the figure revival (described in *Royal Doulton Figures*, Eyles & Dennis, Royal Doulton 1978) prevented him for a long time from doing more than jot down some rough ideas and sketches. He and his staff spent eventually many months in modelling, casting, colouring, glazing and firing experiments before he felt satisfied that he had produced a Character Jug which came up to the standard he had set himself. This was *John Barleycorn* which achieved instant popularity. It was soon followed by *Old Charley*, the night watchman, *Sairey Gamp*, Dickens' bibulous midwife and sick-nurse, *Parson Brown*, the sporting cleric and the notorious *Dick Turpin*, most famous perhaps of all highwaymen. These were the prelude to a whole procession of fascinating character studies evolved by Charles Noke and several of his colleagues and successors.

Two other names which feature predominantly in the early years of the figure-jug revival are those of Leslie Harradine and Harry Fenton. Harradine contributed some brilliant studies of Dickens characters, probably at Noke's specific request – for Dickens, apart from Shakespeare and Burns, was his greatest love in literature. It is believed that Harry Fenton, also a great admirer of Dickens, collaborated with Harradine in the final design of some of these jugs. Fenton himself made brilliant contributions to the range – *John Peel*, *Granny*, *Dick Turpin*, *Old King Cole*, *The Vicar of Bray* and several others.

Harry Fenton first joined Doulton of Burslem in 1903 as an apprentice modeller under Noke. He soon became one of his ablest assistants and was much missed when in 1911 he decided to emigrate to the United States where he became an American citizen. He remained there until 1928, working mostly in Trenton, New Jersey, gaining further experience which stood him in good stead when he returned to England. In 1929 he rejoined Doulton and played an invaluable part not only in the development of the Character Jugs but in the modelling of many of the limited edition presentation jugs – among them the *Regency Coach*, the *George Washington*, *Drake*, *Shakespeare*, *Captain Cook* and *Tower of London* jugs. Many of the limited edition Loving Cups were also his creations in close collaboration with Noke. It is, however, in the Character Jugs that his rare and subtle sense of humour and his knowledge of country types are most clearly shown, imparting a vivid sense of almost living reality. He died in 1953 and his last model, the Character Jug *Johnny Appleseed*, was produced in that year.

Four years before Harry Fenton's death, Max Henk, another talented modeller, had joined the Burslem Pottery, working under the direction of Cecil (Jack) Noke who had succeeded his father as Art Director in 1936. Jack himself was not a modeller and for many years to come the continued and, indeed, ever-growing success of the Character Jugs was largely due to Max Henk's great abilities as a creative ceramic sculptor. His first of many jugs was *Long John Silver*. He came of a distinguished family of ceramic modellers. His great-grandfather, Christian Henk, came from Germany to Minton about 1842; his grandfather, John, born in 1846, was at Minton from 1863 to c.1914; his father, Louis, modelled for Spode and Max himself, before going to Doulton in 1949, was also a modeller at Spode. He retired in 1973.

In recent years, under the direction of Jo Ledger, Design Director, and Eric Griffiths, Art Director of the Ceramic Sculpture Division, a new group of modellers have been ably continuing the tradition, among them Gary Sharp (now no longer at Burslem), David Tootle (a freelance modeller), Alan Moore and Peter Gee. The most prolific so far has been David Brian Biggs, who studied at the Shrewsbury School of Art and joined Royal Doulton at Burslem in 1958 as an assistant to Max Henk. The first of his Character Jugs was *Town Crier* in 1960 and since then he has created some twenty others, including *Regency Beau, Golfer, Jockey, Gardener, Veteran Motorist, Lobster Man, Gulliver* and four of the *Jugs of Williamsburg*.

Thanks to the craftsmanship and versatility of the Royal Doulton modellers, a host of fascinating characters created during the past forty-five years has become available for the collector. In the lists which follow, all available information is given as to the modellers, dates of introduction and withdrawal and, in response to constant requests, notes about some of the characters, real or imaginary, who have inspired Royal Doulton creations in this field.

CHAPTER SIX

How a Character Jug is made

Some of the processes used in making a Character Jug or Toby Jug are basically the same as in the eighteenth century but considerable improvements in technique, and in control of clays, colours, glazes and moulds, have been effected as a result of modern scientific ceramic research. Firing methods have also changed considerably; the coal-fired bottle kilns have been superseded by kilns fired by gas or electricity which can be far more efficiently controlled.

After making preliminary sketches, the modeller creates a prototype of the new model in clay. The modeller is a master-craftsman with a profound knowledge of the potentialities of the ceramic medium. When the clay model has been satisfactorily completed, a master-mould is prepared from it in plaster of Paris; from this, in turn, a working 'case', also in plaster, is produced. It is from this 'case' that all the subsequent working moulds are made. Each of these is used only from twenty-five to thirty times in order to ensure the faultless reproduction of the modeller's original creation.

For the *Long John Silver* jug seven separate pieces are required which have to be most carefully fitted together. Each working mould has an opening into which 'slip' – a liquid mixture of clay and other finely ground ingredients – is poured. The filled moulds are allowed to stand for about an hour, during which time the

1 Every character jug starts life as an idea in an artist's mind. His hands then sculpture a lump of clay into an accurate master model. Here accuracy is vital because the lines and detail of this model will exactly determine the appearance of the finished jug.

2 This picture shows the incredibly detailed moulds which are used to make a character jug.

3 The clay cast of the character jug is carefully removed from the mould.

4 The handle which is cast separately is then stuck to the jug by a highly trained and experienced assembler.

5 Each character jug is then carefully placed on the kiln trolley ready for the first or 'biscuit firing'. During this firing a massive shrinkage of $12\frac{1}{2}$ per cent in volume takes place, a fact for which the mould maker has to allow at the initial stages of making the mould.

porous plaster gradually absorbs the water in the 'slip', leaving a layer of clay adhering to the inner surfaces of the mould. When this layer is judged to be sufficiently thick, the remaining 'slip' is poured off; the various sections of the moulds are removed one by one; and the clay shapes are extracted. The separate parts of the jug are then assembled and joined with the help of a coating of 'slip'.

At this stage, the seams formed by the moulds are carefully removed and the surfaces skilfully sponged to prevent any rough edges. After drying at a controlled temperature in a steam-heated stove, the jugs then receive their first or 'biscuit' firing. During this firing, the temperature reaches $1,160°$ centigrade and the jug shrinks by approximately $12\frac{1}{2}\%$ of its original size in the unfired clay.

After careful inspection, the jug then goes on to the decorating studio. Special ceramic pigments, suitable for underglaze painting, are used; these are painted on by hand by artists of long experience. The colours are then fixed to the 'biscuit' (unglazed) surface by firing in a special type of kiln, called a 'hardening-on' kiln. After the second firing, the jug is glazed by dipping it in a liquid mixture of a glass-like nature. Next comes a third firing – the glost firing – at a temperature slightly below that of the 'biscuit' firing. During this final firing the glaze is indissolubly wedded to the ware, creating a permanent transparent coating, which protects the ceramic colours and, at the same time, subtly enhances their beauty.

1

2

3

4

5

6

7

8

6 After the biscuit firing the jug passes to the hands of the paintress whose careful touches will bring life and colour to the jug.

7 The painted jug is then hand-dipped in a vat of glaze, allowed to dry and re-fired to create the characteristic Doulton sheen.

8 After the final firing in the glost kiln the Royal Doulton character jug has completed its journey. It has been turned from liquid clay into a beautiful collectors' piece.

9 Before a character jug is allowed to leave the factory it is inspected to make sure it is perfect. One crack or flaw, the slightest colour fault, the least blemish in the glaze, and it will never bear the name Royal Doulton or appear in a shop.

9

Character Jugs

Royal Doulton Character and Toby Jugs

Alphabetical List

All Character and Toby Jugs produced by Royal Doulton are illustrated in the following alphabetical list. The large size is shown in each case and is illustrated as near as possible to life size. Where piloted jugs appear to exist in sufficient quantities to interest collectors, they have also been included.

In the list the key-word is the *first* word in the name other than *The*. John Peel, for example, will be found under John; Old King Cole under Old; and Mr Pickwick under Mr.

Only the heights of Toby Jugs are given individually. The larger size Character Jugs vary in height between $5\frac{1}{4}$ and $7\frac{1}{2}$ in (13.3 and 19 cm); the small between $3\frac{1}{4}$ and 4 in (8.8 and 10.1 cm); the miniature between $2\frac{1}{4}$ and $2\frac{1}{2}$ in (5.7 and 6.3 cm). The tinies are c. $1\frac{1}{4}$ in (3.1 cm) high.

Colour and Modelling Changes

Because the Character and Toby Jugs are all individually hand-painted no two are ever exactly alike. Many slight changes in colouring will therefore be noticed which it is impossible to particularise.

A few rather more noticeable alterations in colour and also some changes in modelling and sizes are mentioned in the following alphabetical list.

Between 1968 and 1971, because of major alterations going on at the Burslem factory, the jugs were made in a fine china body instead of the usual fine earthenware. As these were decorated in on-glaze colours and the body was translucent instead of opaque, collectors will notice a difference in the overall effect. As such jugs were made for a period of three years only they are bound to become rare.

Anne Boleyn

Designer: D. Tootle
D.6644 (large)
Introduced 1975; still in production
See remarks under Henry VIII, page 85

Apothecary

Designer: M. Henk
D.6567 (large); D.6574 (small);
D.6581 (miniature)
Introduced 1963; still in production

This is one of the *Character Jugs of Williamsburg*. Named in honour of King William III, eighteenth-century Williamsburg was the capital of Virginia, oldest of the British colonies in America. The small city, which became the political, social and cultural centre of the colony, flourished during a period that forged principles on which subsequent American history was founded. When it ceased to be the seat of government in 1780, Williamsburg lost its position of eminence and fell into decay. Some 35 years ago the decision was taken to restore it as a shrine to American tradition and character, and to reconstruct and refurnish its buildings in their original style.

Side by side with the physical restoration went the re-creation of the spirit of old Williamsburg and its inhabitants. The apothecary and the gunsmith are to be seen at work, costumed in the manner of their forebears. A blacksmith dexterously works with iron in his forge; shoes are made by hand in the bootmaker's shop; the night watchman does his regular rounds. These and other personalities have inspired the creation of the Royal Doulton *Character Jugs of Williamsburg* as a tribute to American history and culture. Their authenticity is vouched for in the approval given by Williamsburg Restoration Incorporated.

Apothecaries or 'potecaries' were predecessors of the modern pharmacists. They prepared and sold drugs for medicinal purposes. In London, in the early seventeenth century, they formed their own company under a charter from King James I. At one time they not only dispensed prescriptions for doctors but they themselves also treated patients.

Aramis

Designer: M. Henk
D.6441 (large); D.6454 (small)
Introduced 1956; still in production
D.6508 (miniature)
Introduced 1960; still in production

Aramis, Porthos and Athos are the valiant trio whose rallying-call was 'All for one, one for all' and whose exciting exploits were first narrated in the famous romance, *The Three Musketeers*, by Alexandre Dumas, published in 1844. In this book and its successors *Thirty Years After* and *The Vicomte de Bragelonne* Dumas recounts the adventures of an impoverished Gascon gentleman, d'Artagnan, who during the reign of Louis XIII, comes to Paris to join the King's Musketeers. At first he becomes embroiled in duels with the three staunch comrades but later is accepted as their friend and shares with them many stirring adventures.

'Ard of 'Earing

Designer: D. Biggs
D.6588 (large); D.6591 (small);
D.6594 (miniature)
Introduced 1964; withdrawn 1967

'Hard of hearing' (implying partially deaf)
occurs in an old nursery rhyme of which
one verse goes:

> 'Old woman, old woman, shall we go a-
> shearing?'
> 'Speak a little louder, sir, I'm very hard of
> hearing!'
> 'Old woman, old woman, shall I love you
> dearly?'
> 'Thank you very kindly, sir, now I hear you
> clearly!'

'Ard of 'earing became a popular catch
word in England in the 1920s after
A. T. Cook, the General Secretary of
the National Union of Mineworkers,
facetiously used it as an excuse for ignoring
the overtures of the Lloyd George
administration.

'Arriet

Designer: H. Fenton
D.6208 (large); D.6236 (small);
D.6250 (miniature)
D.6256 (tiny)
Introduced 1947; withdrawn 1960
There was a colour change in 1951

'Arry and 'Arriet depict London Cockney costermongers. The costermonger is an itinerant street trader who usually displays his wares on a barrow but sometimes uses a cart or a 'donkey-shay!' (The word coster-monger is derived from 'costard' monger – one who sold large apples called costards).

On festive occasions, such as the Lord Mayor's Show, a Coronation or a Jubilee, 'Arry and 'Arriet adorn themselves with pearl buttons and 'Arriet puts on her best hat with the ostrich feathers. Pearl buttons were in fact indicated as part of the decoration of these two characters as originally designed. For some unknown reason they were omitted when the jugs were put into general production, and only a small quantity were made with buttons. Although now very rare, these can be found in different sizes and colours (blue and brown).

'Arry

Designer: H. Fenton
D.6207 (large); D.6235 (small);
D.6249 (miniature); D.6255 (tiny)
Introduced 1947; withdrawn 1960.
There was a colour change in 1951
See remarks under 'Arriet on previous
page

Size and colour variations of 'Arry with
buttons

Athos

Designer: M. Henk
D.6439 (large); D.6452 (small)
Introduced 1956; still in production
D.6509 (miniature)
Introduced 1960; still in production
See remarks under Aramis, page 43

Auld Mac

Designer: H. Fenton
D.5823 (large); D.5824 (small)
Introduced 1938; still in production
D.6253 (miniature)
Introduced 1946; still in production
D.6257 (tiny)
Introduced 1946; withdrawn 1960

Between 1938 and c.1945 this model was also known as 'Owd Mac'

Auld Mac has been the subject of numerous anecdotes about the canny, thrifty Scot as popularly conceived (or misconceived!). In one music hall song popularised by Sir Harry Lauder he tells of a visit to London during which, before he had even time to turn round, 'bang went saxpence'. This phrase is impressed on the jug.

48

Bacchus

Designer: M. Henk
D.6499 (large); D.6505 (small)
Introduced 1959; still in production
D.6521 (miniature)
Introduced 1960; still in production

Bacchus or Dionysus, 'the god of wine', was an ancient Greek deity whose rites were particularly associated with the grape-harvest. He represented the productive and exhilarating forces of nature and became the object of a popular cult whose devotees, intoxicated with wine, often went into mystic frenzies during which they believed themselves one with their god.

Beefeater

Designer: H.Fenton
D.6206 (large); D.6233 (small);
D.6251 (miniature)
Introduced 1947; still in production
In 1953 the Royal Cypher GR (George
Rex) on the handle was changed to ER
(Elizabeth Regina)

The popular name for a member of the Queen's Bodyguard of the Yeomen of the Guard is 'Beefeater'. The Yeomen of the Guard were founded by Henry VII in 1485 after the Battle of Bosworth and consisted originally of his private guard who had helped him to the throne. The first permanent Royal Guard, their duty in earlier times was to protect the Sovereign's person; now their functions are solely ceremonial – being present on State occasions, searching the vaults of the Houses of Parliament on Guy Fawkes' Day, and so forth. They rank as members of the Royal Household.

The Yeomen of the Guard and the Yeomen Warders of the Tower of London (also nicknamed 'Beefeaters') wear the style of uniform of the Tudor period.

Blacksmith

Designer: D. Biggs
D.6571 (large); D.6578 (small);
D.6585 (miniature)
Introduced 1963; still in production
One of the *Character Jugs of Williams-
burg;* see remarks under Apothecary,
page 42

Bootmaker

Designer: D. Biggs
D.6572 (large); D.6579 (small);
D.6586 (miniature)
Introduced 1963: still in production
Another *Character Jug of Williamsburg*;
see remarks under Apothecary, page 42

Buz Fuz

Designers: L. Harradine and
H. Fenton
D.5838 (special size)
Introduced 1938; withdrawn 1948
D.5838 (small size)
Introduced 1948; withdrawn 1960
This jug was first made in an inter-
mediate size, c. 4½in (11 cm), between
the usual large and small sizes. It was
scaled down in 1948

Mr Sergeant or Serjeant Buz Fuz is the
bullying barrister in Charles Dickens'
Pickwick Papers, published 1836–37. The
Widow Bardell, completely misinterpret-
ing Mr Pickwick's innocent intentions,
sues him for breach of promise. Buz Fuz
acts as her counsel and secures judgement
in her favour with damages of £750. He is
described as 'cozening or browbeating
intelligent juries as occasion serves; the
legalised champion of broken-hearted
widows; adored of solicitors and constant
recipient of highly marked briefs'.

Sergeants (or serjeants) in the legal
sense were, until 1875, barristers who
enjoyed certain privileges of precedence
over other barristers.

Captain Ahab

Designer: G.Sharp
D.6500 (large); D.6506 (small)
Introduced 1959; still in production
D.6522 (miniature)
Introduced 1960; still in production

Captain Ahab is the central character in Herman Melville's epic masterpiece, *Moby Dick*, published in 1851. Moby Dick is a ferocious and cunning great white whale which has brought disaster to many of its pursuers and has deprived Ahab himself of a leg. His fixed obsession – to find the whale and take his revenge – leads to his death and the destruction of his ship with all its crew, save one survivor.

Cap'n Cuttle

Designer: L. Harradine and H. Fenton
D.5842 (special size)
Introduced 1938; withdrawn 1948
D.5842 (small size)
Introduced 1948; withdrawn 1960
See note under Buz Fuz re scaling
down

Captain Edward Cuttle is a character in
one of Charles Dickens' best-known novels,
Dombey and Son. The favourite saying of
this simple-minded but lovable mariner
was 'When found, make a note of.'

He had a well-nigh religious dread of
the terrible Mrs MacStinger, and a profound respect for the learning and genius of
Sol Gills.

Captain Henry Morgan

Designer: G. Sharp
D.6467 (large); D.6469 (small)
Introduced 1958; still in production
D.6510 (miniature)
Introduced 1960; still in production

Captain Morgan (later Sir Henry Morgan) was born c.1635 in Glamorganshire, of good Welsh stock. It seems that he was kidnapped as a youth at Bristol and shipped to Barbados. He became the most famous buccaneer of his age, conducting in the Caribbean many triumphant expeditions against the Spanish possessions in and around that area. In 1671 he captured and plundered Panama. He was knighted by King Charles II and made Lieutenant-Governor of Jamaica. He died in 1688.

Captain Hook

Designers: M. Henk and D. Biggs
D.6597 (large); D.6601 (small);
D.6605 (miniature)
Introduced 1965; withdrawn 1971

Hook, the villainous pirate captain in Sir James M. Barrie's *Peter Pan* was so named because of the dangerous hook he used in place of his missing hand. He is one of the less pleasant characters whom the motherless Peter and his companions encounter in Never-Never land but fortunately he is always thwarted in his attempts to do harm.

Cardinal

Designer: C. J. Noke
D.5614 (large) Introduced 1936;
withdrawn 1960
D.6033 (small)
Introduced 1939; withdrawn 1960
D.6129 (miniature)
Introduced 1940; withdrawn 1960
D.6258 (tiny)
Introduced 1947; withdrawn 1960

The Cardinal is a dignitary of the Catholic Church who ranks next to the Pope. International usage accords him the precedence of a royal prince. His title, which is derived from the Latin for a *hinge*, was first given in the fifth century to the clergy in charge of certain parishes around which the local religious life of Rome turned. The importance of the Cardinals was rapidly enhanced when their right of electing the Pope was secured against the encroachments of the Emperor. They are counsellors of the Pope on decisions of world-wide influence, and thus the interests that *hinge* on the present-day Cardinals, who represent many different nations, are more important than ever before.

It is possible that this jug represents Cardinal Wolsey, for it has features in common with Noke's figure model of the actor Henry Irving playing the part of Wolsey in Shakespeare's *Henry VIII*.

Catherine Howard

Designer: P. Gee
D.6645 (large)
Introduced 1978; still in production
See remarks under Henry VIII, page
85

Catherine of Aragon

Designer: A. Maslankowski
D.6643 (large)
Introduced 1975; still in production
See remarks under Henry VIII, page
85

The Cavalier

Designer: H. Fenton
D.6114 (large)
Introduced 1940; withdrawn 1960
D.6173 (small)
Introduced 1941; withdrawn 1960
There was a slight colour change in
1950 and the collar was also altered.
Early models feature a goatee beard.

In days gone by the Cavalier was a horse-
man, particularly a horse-soldier, or a man
of gentle birth trained in knightly exercises.
The term was also applied to a gallant
especially when escorting a lady. 'Cavalier',
in early English, was sometimes used in a
contemptuous sense to describe an over-
bearing, haughty, offhand character but the
name was adopted as a title of honour by
the supporters of King Charles I in the
Civil War against the Puritan Roundheads.
At the Restoration of the Monarchy in
1660 the Court preserved the name.

Early version of *Cavalier*, showing the
goatee beard

Churchill

Designer: C.J. Noke
D.6170 (large)
Introduced 1940 and probably withdrawn a year or two later.

An unusual plain cream-coloured jug with two black handles. The base bears the wording: 'WINSTON SPENCER CHURCHILL PRIME MINISTER OF BRITAIN 1940: THIS LOVING CUP WAS MADE DURING THE 'BATTLE OF BRITAIN' AS A TRIBUTE TO A GREAT LEADER.' A similar jug was produced by Minton, modelled by Eric Owen.

This was a somewhat poor likeness of Churchill and apparently it was discreetly suggested to Doulton by a distinguished friend of the Chairman that it should be withdrawn.

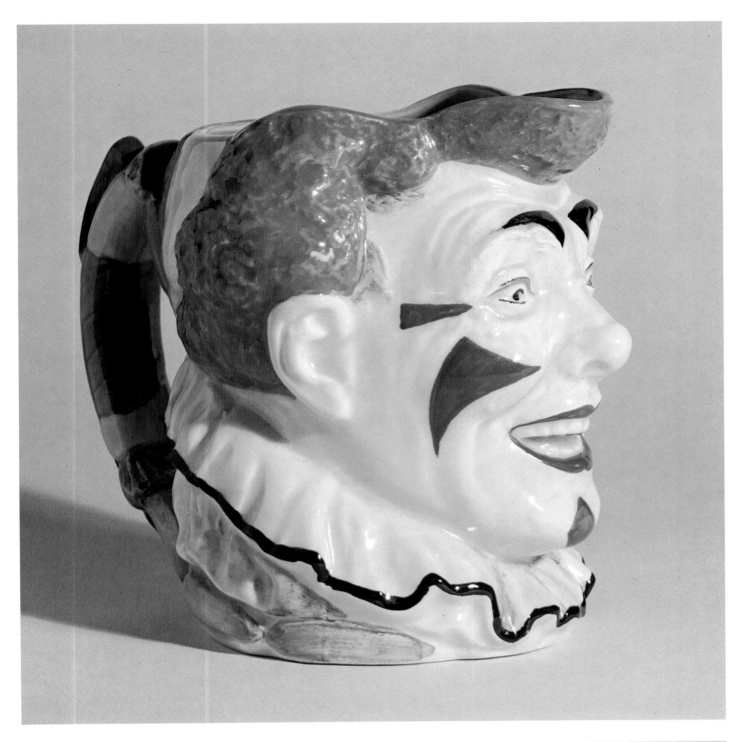

Clown (orange hair)

Designer: H. Fenton
D.5610 (large)
Introduced 1937; withdrawn c. 1942

Originally a clumsy yokel or buffoon in traditional Italian comedy, Shakespeare transformed him in *Twelfth Night* and above all in *King Lear* from a despised and vulgar entertainer into an important element in the drama. The clown continues to appear in circus and pantomime today. His traditional make-up and false nose recall his rustic origins.

Clown (white hair)

Designer: H. Fenton
D.6322 (large)
Introduced 1951; withdrawn 1955

Dick Turpin (first version)

Designers C. J. Noke and H. Fenton
D.5485 (large)
Introduced 1935; withdrawn 1960
D.5618 (small)
Introduced 1936; withdrawn 1960
D.6128 (miniature)
Introduced 1940; withdrawn 1960
This early version shows Dick without
a mask and with a pistol-shaped handle

Dick Turpin was one of the most notorious
of English eighteenth-century highwaymen. He was born at Hempstead, near
Saffron Walden, Essex, in 1706. He joined
a gang of deer-stealers and smugglers in
Essex and later went into partnership with
Tom King, another well-known highwayman whom he accidentally shot dead.

To avoid arrest he left Essex for
Lincolnshire and Yorkshire and set up
under an assumed name as a horse dealer.
He was eventually caught, convicted and
hanged at York on April 7th, 1739. Popular
legend has endowed him with heroic and
romantic qualities which he does not
appear to have deserved. The famous ride
to York on his horse Black Bess is pure
fiction and was invented by Harrison
Ainsworth in his romance *Rookwood*.

Dick Turpin (second version)

Designer D.Biggs
D.6528 (large); D.6535 (small);
D.6542 (miniature)
Introduced 1960; still in production
This new version shows Dick wearing a
mask. The handle is in the shape of a
horse's head.
See remarks under Dick Turpin (first
version)

Dick Whittington

Designer: M. Henk
D.6375 (large)
Introduced 1953; withdrawn 1960

No Lord Mayor of London has so excited the imagination of his fellow-citizens as Richard Whittington (c.1359–1423), son of Sir William de Whyttyngton, Lord of the Manor of Pauntley in Gloucestershire. By trade a mercer, he achieved great commercial success and was able to make extensive loans to Kings Richard II, Henry IV and Henry V. He was famous for his charity and endowed many libraries, almshouses, colleges and churches. During his long civic career he was Lord Mayor of London three times. Whittington became a folk-hero to the people of London who embroidered the story of his life with all manner of legends, including the one beloved by children and pantomime-goers of how he was led to his high destiny by his pet cat. This romantic story first appeared in a ballad in 1605.

Don Quixote

Designer: G. Blower
D.6455 (large); D6460 (small)
Introduced 1957; still in production
D.6511 (miniature)
Introduced 1960; still in production

Don Quixote is the absurd yet sympathetic central character in Miguel de Cervantes' renowned novel of the same name, universally regarded as a masterpiece of European literature. The first part was published in 1605, the second ten years later.

Don Quixote de la Mancha is a gallant, high-minded, amiable and otherwise sane knight who has had his imagination disastrously disordered by listening to too many improbable romances. He roams the world, clad in rusty armour and riding on his old horse, Rosinante, in search of chivalrous adventures. Accompanied by his more down-to-earth squire, Sancho Panza, whom he has enticed to accompany him with the prospect of becoming governor of an island, he involves himself in all manner of absurd adventures. To his disordered mind ordinary objects, such as windmills,

assume terrifying or romantic forms. He idealises a plain country wench of a neighbouring village and elevates her (she being quite unaware of the fact) into the mistress of his heart under the high-sounding title of Dulcinea del Toboso.

The story, a kind of burlesque of the romances of chivalry, is full of sound philosophy, masterly dialogue and shrewd commentary on life. The character of Don Quixote contains more than a touch of the author himself who had many disappointments both in his career and in love.

Drake

Designer: H. Fenton
D.6115 (large)
Introduced 1940; withdrawn 1960
D.6174 (small)
Introduced 1941, withdrawn 1960
There was a colour change in 1950
An early version without a hat was
piloted but did not go into general
production. A few examples exist

Sir Francis Drake (c.1545–96) is one of the
outstanding figures in the history of British
sea-power. A Devonshire man, he took
part in several expeditions against the
Spaniards in the West Indies and the
'Spanish Main' in Central America, bring-
ing back much booty. Between December
1577 and September 1580 he completed a
voyage round the world (the first Englishman to accomplish this feat) in the *Golden
Hind* and was later knighted by Queen
Elizabeth I on board this ship.

In 1588 a vast fleet, the Spanish Armada,
sailed for England. Drake, as Vice-Admiral
of the Fleet under Lord Howard of Effing-
ham was largely responsible for its defeat;
only some 60 out of 130 ships ever returned
to Spain.

The authenticity of his famous remark
on the bowling green of Plymouth Hoe:
'We have time to finish the game and beat
the Spaniards afterwards' has been
questioned. It may well be true even
though it did not appear in print until
many years later. It is certainly fully in
keeping with the style and spirit of the man
whose exploits still kindle the imagination
nearly four centuries afterwards.

The early, hatless version of *Drake*, inscribed,
Drake he was a Devon man

Falconer

Designer: M. Henk
D.6533 (large); D.6540 (small);
D.6547 (miniature)
Introduced 1960; still in production

The Falconer is skilled in the long and difficult art of training falcons and hawks for chase. Falconry is of very ancient origin, having been known to the Chinese as long ago as 2000 BC. It was practised in many parts of Europe and Asia. In England it was a favourite sport of Ethelbert and other Saxon Kings. From the time of the Norman Conquest in 1066 up to the seventeenth century, kings, princes, lords and ladies took part in the chase, Henry VIII, Elizabeth I and James I being particularly enthusiastic devotees. In Norman times only those of high rank were allowed to keep falcons; the privilege was extended to all freemen in the reign of King John.

With the introduction of fowling-pieces falconry gradually declined in Europe. Nowadays it is carried on mostly in Arabia, Persia, India and China. In some parts of Asia even eagles are trained to attack large game such as antelopes.

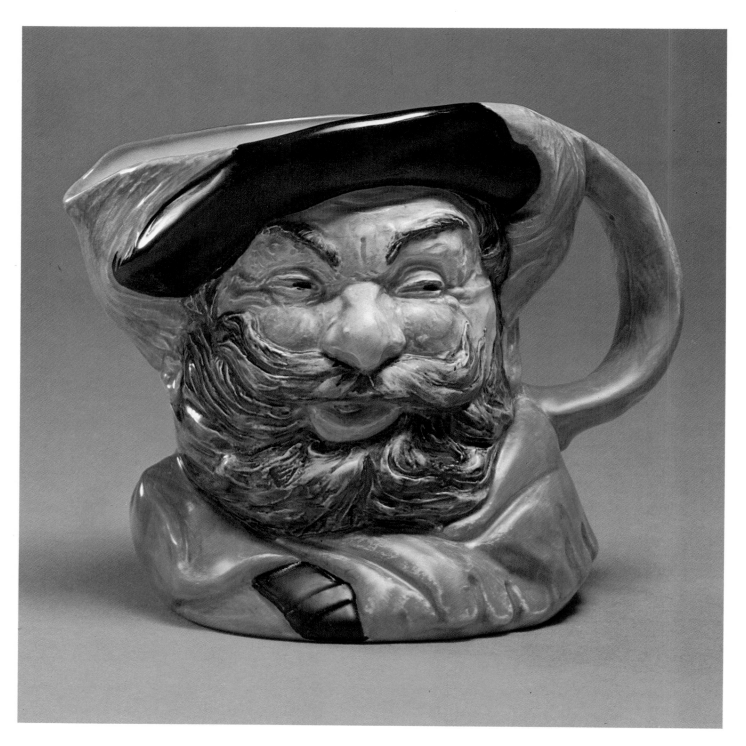

Falstaff

Designer: H. Fenton
D.6287 (large); D.6385 (small)
Introduced 1950; still in production
D.6519 (miniature)
Introduced 1960; still in production
The Doulton catalogue for 1976 was
mistaken in stating only 'Two Sizes';
this should have referred to the Toby
Jug of the same name.

No character could have a better right to be
represented in the Royal Doulton range
than Sir John Falstaff. A lovable rogue, full
of 'tricks and devices' he sees the world –
including himself – as a natural object for
wit and laughter. He would like to see
himself as an innocent man in a world of
villains but in more objective mood has to
confess that he has 'more flesh than another
man; and therefore more frailty'.

In the original draft of *Henry IV, Part
One*, Shakespeare gave him the name of the
Lollard martyr, Oldcastle, but because of
protests from the Oldcastle family sub-
stituted the name Sir John Falstaff. Falstaff
appears also in *The Merry Wives of Windsor*
written, so it is said, within a fortnight, to
meet a command from Queen Elizabeth I
to show Falstaff in love. It is generally
agreed that in this play Falstaff is but a
shadow of his former self.

Farmer John

Designer: C. J. Noke
D.5788 (large); D.5789 (small)
Introduced 1938; withdrawn 1960

Modelled in similar vein to John Barleycorn, this jug portrays the traditional farmer
of English folk-songs, nursery rhymes and
country lore. Happy, despite many
grumbles about weather (which is never
what he wants) and all manner of other
trials, he usually manages to eat and drink
well, and is the life and soul of the party
when he presides over a 'harvest home' or
similar festivity.

Fat Boy

Designers: L. Harradine and
H. Fenton
D.5840 (special size)
Introduced 1938, withdrawn 1948
D.5840 (small size)
Introduced 1948; withdrawn 1960
D.6139 (miniature); D.6142 (tiny)
Introduced 1940; withdrawn 1960
See note under Buz Fuz re scaling
down of original intermediate size

The Fat Boy, one of Charles Dickens'
inimitable characters depicted in the
Pickwick Papers, is always on the verge of
slumbering placidly and stolidly in any
position, despite the loudly renewed calls
of old Wardle, his master. Only the magic
lure of eatables and drinkables can expel
the somnolency from his rotund form. His
smile and downward-looking gaze, as
portrayed on the jug, are doubtless
occasioned by his anticipation of a large
helping of rook pie.

The Fortune Teller

Designer: G. Sharp
D.6497 (large); D.6503 (small)
Introduced 1959; withdrawn 1967
D.6523 (miniature)
Introduced 1960; withdrawn 1967

The traditional type of fortune teller depicted by this Doulton jug is a Romany or gipsy. 'Cross her hand with a piece of silver' and she will reveal your future – or as much of it as she thinks fit – by reading your palm, translating the cards or the tea-leaves, or gazing in her crystal ball. For centuries gipsies have wandered Europe, being particularly associated in the popular mind with fairground booths, 'Derby Day' and similar occasions. The genuine gipsy fortune-teller is becoming ever harder to find but she has many imitators.

Friar Tuck

Designer: H. Fenton
D.6321 (large)
Introduced 1951; withdrawn 1960

A man of girth and mirth who liked his venison pasties washed down with a stoup of pilfered sack, Friar Tuck was the outlaw's genial chaplain and father confessor in the Robin Hood cycle of ballads. He does not appear at all in the earliest ballads and was probably introduced when Morris dancing became a feature of the traditional Robin Hood games.

Friar Tuck figures in Sir Walter Scott's *Ivanhoe* and Thomas Love Peacock's *Maid Marian*. The oak-tree handle and acorns depicted on the jug recall the fat, jovial and pugnacious friar's reputed adventures in Nottingham Forest where the outlaws lived in hiding from the Sheriff and his men.

Gaoler

Designer: D. Biggs
D.6570 (large); D.6577 (small);
D.6584 (miniature)
Introduced 1963; still in production
A Character Jug of Williamsburg; see
remarks under Apothecary, page 42

Gardener

Designer: D. Biggs
D.6630 (large); D.6634 (small);
D.6638 (miniature)
Introduced 1973; still in production

One of those jugs which scarcely call for comment. A type that is rapidly disappearing in these days when knowledgeable help in the garden is becoming more and more difficult to find! One can well believe that this character 'knew his onions', not to mention his marrows and other prize-winning garden produce.

Gladiator

Designer: M. Henk
D.6550 (large); D.6553 (small);
D.6556 (miniature)
Introduced 1961; withdrawn 1967

Gladiators were professional fighters, often prisoners of war or slaves, who during the reigns of many of the Roman Emperors were trained to fight each other or wild animals at public shows. Although the word comes from the Latin *gladius* meaning a sword, they fought with various weapons, on foot or on horseback, and sometimes in chariots. They were owned by the State or by private citizens and had to take an oath 'to fight to the death'. If they showed cowardice they were often tortured and killed. If a gladiator was badly wounded he was allowed to lift up his forefinger as a sign that he was begging for mercy. If the populace felt he had put up a good show and deserved to be spared they would wave their handkerchiefs; otherwise they turned their thumbs down.

Golfer

Designer: D. Biggs
D.6623 (large)
Introduced 1971; still in production
Small and miniature sizes were piloted
but not produced

Here we have another character well able to speak for himself and give a detailed stroke by stroke account of his exploits on the links. Golf has well been called one of the most delightful yet exasperating games ever devised by the wit of man. Its effects on the feelings can at times be devastating, at other times exhilarating.

One of the most popular games in the world, with both sexes, it is unusual in that more people play it than watch it and that it can be played from one's youth into the seventies and even beyond.

Nobody is quite sure where the game began. Some say Ancient Rome, others medieval Holland. It was so popular in Scotland that in 1457 the Scottish parliament forbade it because it was interfering with the martial art of archery. Despite that it became what many Scots regard as their national game. It has become equally popular in the United States and many other countries.

Gondolier

Designer: D. Biggs
D.6589 (large); D.6592 (small);
D.6595 (miniature)
Introduced 1964; withdrawn 1969

Gondoliers are the famous singing boat-
men of Venice featured in many a romantic
film. They stand on the 'poppa' in the stern
of the long, narrow, flat-bottomed boats
which they propel with graceful strokes of a
single oar.

The comic operetta, *The Gondoliers*, by
Sir William Gilbert and Sir Arthur
Sullivan, was a great success when first
produced in 1889 and has ever since been
widely and constantly performed both by
professional companies and local groups of
amateurs.

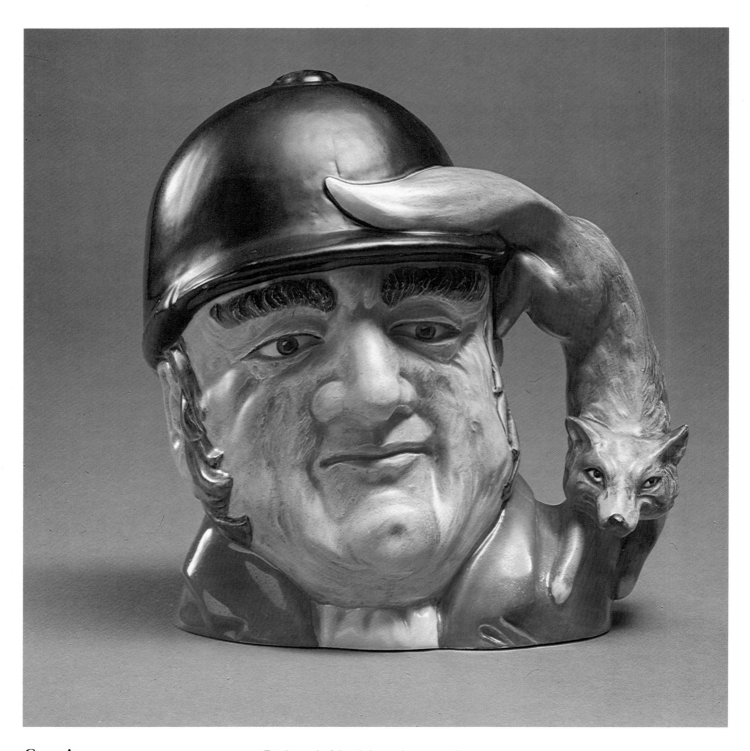

Gone Away

Designer: G. Sharp
D.6531 (large); D.6538 (small);
D.6545 (miniature)
Introduced 1960; still in production

By the end of the eighteenth century the fox had to a large extent replaced both the stag and the hare as the favourite quarry of the chase. Since then hardly any other sport has inspired so many artists.

Here we have a traditional huntsman in red coat and silk hat. He encourages the hounds by horn and voice. The wily Reynard is usually too swift to be coursed by sight and is hunted by scent. Sometimes the hounds lose the scent temporarily but pick it up again; sometimes they lose it altogether. The fox with its cunning, speed and endurance can tax the stamina and patience of his pursuers to such a degree that he escapes capture.

There is much controversy as to whether or not fox hunting should be prohibited by law. Devotees argue that it is less cruel than any alternative method suggested for keeping the fox population in check.

Granny

Designers: H. Fenton and M. Henk
D.5521 (large)
Introduced 1935; still in production
D.6384 (small)
Introduced 1953; still in production
D.6520 (miniature)
Introduced 1960; still in production

H. Fenton designed and modelled the large size, Max Henk the others. The early version of this jug was modelled without the prominent front tooth.

GRANNY
'Life has etched upon her face
Lines of wisdom through the years.
Joys and sorrows, laughter, tears –
She's known them all
And when you're small,
How comforting to be
Curled up safely on her knee'

O.E.E.

Early version of *Granny*, without the prominent front tooth

Guardsman

Designer: M. Henk
D.6568 (large); D.6575 (small);
D.6582 (miniature)
Introduced 1963; still in production
A Character Jug of Williamsburg; see
remarks under Apothecary, page 42

Gulliver

Designer: D. Biggs
D.6560 (large); D.6563 (small);
D. 6566 (miniature)
Introduced 1962; withdrawn 1967

Gulliver's Travels written by Jonathan Swift, Dean of St Patrick's Cathedral, Dublin, and published in 1726, recounts the extraordinary exploits of the seafarer, Lemuel Gulliver, in several strange lands and among their even stranger inhabitants. Although it soon became (and has remained) a popular children's book as a tale of fantasy and adventure, it was really conceived by Swift as a satirical attack on the politicians, scientists and philosophers of his epoch.

On the top of the handle of the jug two diminutive Lilliputians are depicted raising a lock of Gulliver's hair.

Gunsmith

Designer: D. Biggs
D.6573 (large); D.6580 (small);
D.6587 (miniature)
Introduced 1963; still in production
Another *Character Jug of Williamsburg*;
see remarks under Apothecary, page 42

Henry VIII

Designer: E. Griffiths
D.6642 (large)
Introduced 1975; still in production
D.6647 (small); D.6648 (miniature)
Introduced 1979; still in production

Second son of Henry VII, founder of the Tudor dynasty, Henry VIII ruled England from 1509 to 1547. In early manhood he was admired as the most handsome, gay and accomplished prince of his time, well skilled in music, theology, sport, archery and jousting, but in later life he became obese, coarse and ungainly. A staunch Catholic, he wrote a book on the sacraments, refuting the reformer Luther's views, and received from Pope Leo X the title 'Defender of the Faith' which has been borne by all his successors to this day, as witness the initials 'F.D.' on the present British coinage – (Fidei Defensor).

Henry's elder brother Arthur, the heir to the throne, died in 1502 and seven years later, soon after his accession to the throne, Henry married Arthur's widow, Catherine of Aragon, daughter of Ferdinand and Isabella of Spain. This was a step fraught

with fateful consequences.

Disturbed because by 1523, Catherine – now nearing 40 – had provided no male heir (all her children except one daughter, Mary, having been either still-born or having died in infancy) Henry tried through his Lord Chancellor, Cardinal Wolsey, to persuade the Pope to annul the marriage. His argument was that he had broken the Divine Law by wedding his brother's widow and that the death of so many of his children was a judgement upon him. How far he was sincere in this belated penitence and how far he was influenced by the fact that he had fallen in love with one of Catherine's ladies-in-waiting, Anne Boleyn, is a matter for argument. What is certain, is that the Pope's refusal to declare the marriage null and void led, among other consequences, to the fall of Wolsey, the abolition of the Pope's authority in the

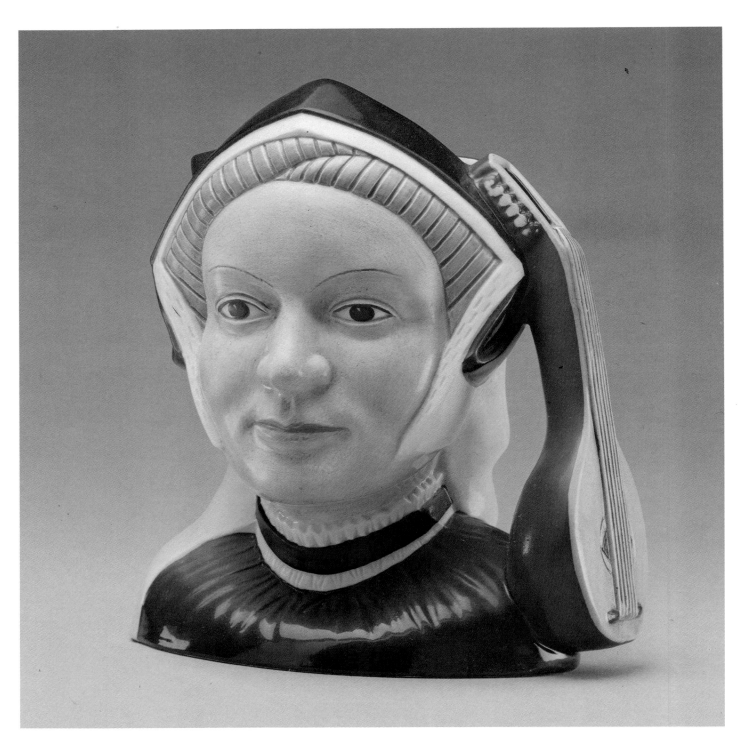

affairs of the English church, the exile of Catherine to a convent, the declaration by parliament that Henry was 'Supreme Head of the Church of England' (to deny which was treason) and the Dissolution of the Monasteries.

Henry had secretly married Anne in January 1533 and in May that year Archbishop Cranmer dutifully declared her Henry's legal wife. She was then crowned with great splendour in Westminster Hall. A child – later to become Elizabeth I – was born in September 1533. Three years later Anne bore a still-born son.

Within a few months of his marriage to Anne, Henry's ardour is said to have already begun to cool. Her failure to produce a male heir perhaps helped to seal her fate. She was accused of adultery with five different men, including her own brother, and on 19th May 1536 she was beheaded in a courtyard of the Tower of London. Next day, Henry married his new love, Jane Seymour, at Hampton Court. It seems that Henry showed true affection to Jane and her death in 1537, soon after having borne a son – later Edward VI – was a real blow to him.

A fourth wife, Anne of Cleves, was too plain for his liking and was quickly divorced; *she* appears to have contrived to remain on good terms with Henry. Catherine Howard, the fifth wife, met the same fate as Anne Boleyn, but the sixth, Catherine Parr, who had already buried two husbands, managed to outlive Henry and within a fortnight married again for the fourth time.

The jug was modelled after the famous painting of Henry by Holbein.

Jane Seymour

Designer: M. Abberley
D.6646 (large)
Introduced 1979; still in production.
See remarks under Henry VIII.

Izaac Walton

Designer: H. Fenton
D.6404 (large)
Introduced towards end of 1953; still in
production

One of the last jugs modelled by Harry
Fenton, this was produced in 1953 to
commemorate the 250th anniversary of
Izaak Walton's death in December 1683
and the 300th anniversary of the publication of *The Compleat Angler*. The features
are based on a portrait by the Flemish
painter, Jacob Huysmans, the original of
which is in the National Portrait Gallery,
London.

Izaak Walton was a personality whose
unique gifts have endeared him to multi-
tudes of both literary and piscatorial
admirers. In 1653, at the age of sixty, he
published the first edition of his most
famous work, *The Compleat Angler*. This
describes, mostly in the form of conversa-
tions between the author and his friends,
the delights of angling and the English
countryside, with many homely philosophical asides and, in Walton's own
words, much 'innocent, harmless mirth'.

Walton continued to add to it until in
1676, in the fifth edition, the thirteen
chapters of the original had grown to
twenty-one. A second part was added by
his fellow-angler, Charles Cotton, who
took up the principal character, Venator,
where Walton had left him.

It has been said of Izaak Walton that
there is hardly a name in English literature,
even of the first rank, whose immortality is
more secure, or whose personality is the
subject of a more enthusiastic cult.

Jarge

Designer: H. Fenton
D.6288 (large); D.6295 (small)
Introduced 1950; withdrawn 1960

Jarge has well been described as 'the
archetypal country bumpkin'. Not the
handsomest of fellows – with a proclivity
for straw sucking that can become irritating
if indulged in to excess – yet when there is
work to be done in the fields he may very
likely be found behind a haystack with a
milkmaid. Perhaps that is why two
entwined hearts feature on this jug!

Jester

Designer: C. J. Noke
D.5556 (small)
Introduced 1936; withdrawn 1960

The Jester was originally a minstrel or reciter of *gestes* – legendary tales, high adventures and romances. He later became a merry-andrew or wit kept by the royal courts and noble households of medieval times for their amusement. Although his origins can be traced back to India, Arabia and Greece, it was probably in Saxon times that he first appeared in England, his role being to amuse his listeners with witty remarks. In his motley attire, with a kind of cowl falling over his shoulders, he was a familiar figure in the English Court up to the time of Cromwell. After the Restoration of Charles II he lingered on for a few decades in wealthy private households.

Jockey

Designer: D. Biggs
D.6625 (large)
Introduced 1971; withdrawn 1975
A small and a miniature size were
piloted but not put into production

To be a jockey, urging on an immaculate
thoroughbred across the green turf and
leaving all his rivals behind, is often the
dream or wishful thinking of the punter
who has left more money in the book-
maker's satchel than he has taken out.
Wistfully he imagines future triumphs at
Newmarket, Epsom or some other big
race-meeting.

John Barleycorn

Designer: C. J. Noke
D.5327 (large)
Introduced 1934; withdrawn 1960
D.5735 (small)
Introduced 1937; withdrawn 1960
D.6041 (miniature)
Introduced 1939; withdrawn 1960
Early models were produced with a
different handle

This, the first Character jug produced in
the Royal Doulton range, was re-issued in
1978 for sale in North America in a limited
edition of 7,500. This re-issue carried a
special backstamp stating the number and
Special Exhibition Reproduction.

John Barleycorn, a familiar figure in old

English ballads and tracts, personifies the
malt liquor made from barley. Sometimes
he appears as a knight, as in the tract *The
Arraining and Indicting of Sir John
Barleycorn, Knt.*, printed for Timothy
Tosspot (surely another of the Toby
fraternity), and in *A Pleasant New Ballad of
the Bloody Murther of Sir John Barleycorn.*

He has often been invoked as a hero of
agrarian revolt – for instance by the
Luddites who tried to stem the tide of
industrialisation by breaking up machinery
in 1812.

Robert Burns in a ballad of the same
name represents John Barleycorn as being
crushed between two millstones – hence
the shape of the jug. Charles Noke probably
took the idea from a Lambeth salt-glaze
stoneware jug, made in the nineteenth
century, in much the same vein but considerably larger, or from one of the many

Barleycorn jugs modelled by the Martin
Brothers.

Early version of *John Barleycorn*, showing
the different handle

John Peel

Designer: H. Fenton
D.5612 (large)
Introduced 1936; withdrawn 1960
D.5731 (small)
Introduced 1937; withdrawn 1960
D.6130 (miniature)
Introduced 1940; withdrawn 1960
D.6259 (tiny)
Introduced 1947; withdrawn 1960

John Peel, a Cumberland yeoman with a passion for fox-hunting, has been immortalised in the song *D'ye ken John Peel*, written by John Woodcock Graves about 1826. He is shown in traditional fox-hunting attire; the handle of the jug is in the form of a hunting-crop.

In *Songs and Ballads of Cumberland*, published in 1866, Mr Graves explained that the song was written impromptu, in John Peel's presence, to an old air, *Bonnie Annie* or *Cannie Annie*. After singing it through for the first time, Graves turned to Peel and said: 'By jove, Peel, you'll be sung when we're both run to earth!!'

Johnny Appleseed

Designer: H. Fenton
D.6372 (large)
Introduced 1953; withdrawn 1969

Johnny Appleseed was the nickname of John Chapman (c.1775–1843), a famous New England character, who spent his boyhood days in Longmeadow, Massachusetts, USA, where he read and heard about, and longed for, the Western forests. Later on, he travelled on foot through Ohio, Pennsylvania, Indiana and Illinois, planting appleseeds near settlers' cabins. Many stories are told of his remarkable woodcraft. It was said that he made the Indians his friends and that wild beasts never harmed him. His constant companions were his Bible, John Bunyan's *Pilgrim's Progress* and Aesop's *Fables*.

Johnny Appleseed, a major American folk-lore hero, is the subject of a ballad by W. H. Venable, and of several poems by Vachel Lindsay including the well-known *In Praise of Johnny Appleseed*.

Lawyer

Designer: M. Henk
D.6498 (large); D.6504 (small)
Introduced 1959; still in production
D.6524 (miniature)
Introduced 1960; still in production

Our feeling about lawyers is apt to depend
on whether they are for us or against us.
Dick the Butcher in Shakespeare's
Henry VI Part II had no doubt about *his*
views. 'The first thing we do', he says to
Jack Cade, 'let's kill all the lawyers.'

Max Henk's lawyer, however, looks
genial enough, having probably wined and
dined well at *The Wig and Pen* or some
other well-known hostelry, after winning a
tricky case on some obscure point of law
that nobody had heard of for two centuries.

Lobster Man

Designer: D. Biggs
D.6617 (large); D.6620 (small)
Introduced 1968; still in production

'The day had been quite perfect with radiant sun on an azure sea. The gulls wheeling over our cottage. The ever-changing colours of the mountains. And now it was nightfall and all was still save for the lapping of the water and the gentle splash of oars as the Lobster Man set his pots. In the morning he would collect his bounty and with luck would drop one in for us.'
(From *Memories of Ireland* by O.E.E.)

Long John Silver

Designer: M. Henk
D.6335 (large); D.6386 (small)
Introduced 1952; still in production
D.6512 (miniature)
Introduced 1960; still in production

Of all the fictional buccaneers that ever sailed the high seas under the 'Jolly Roger', probably none is better known than Long John Silver, a famous character in Robert Louis Stevenson's *Treasure Island*. Who would have dreamt that this broad-faced, kindly-looking seaman could raise a desperate gang of mutineers and lead the crew of the *Hispaniola* into such perilous adventures in their search for buried treasure!

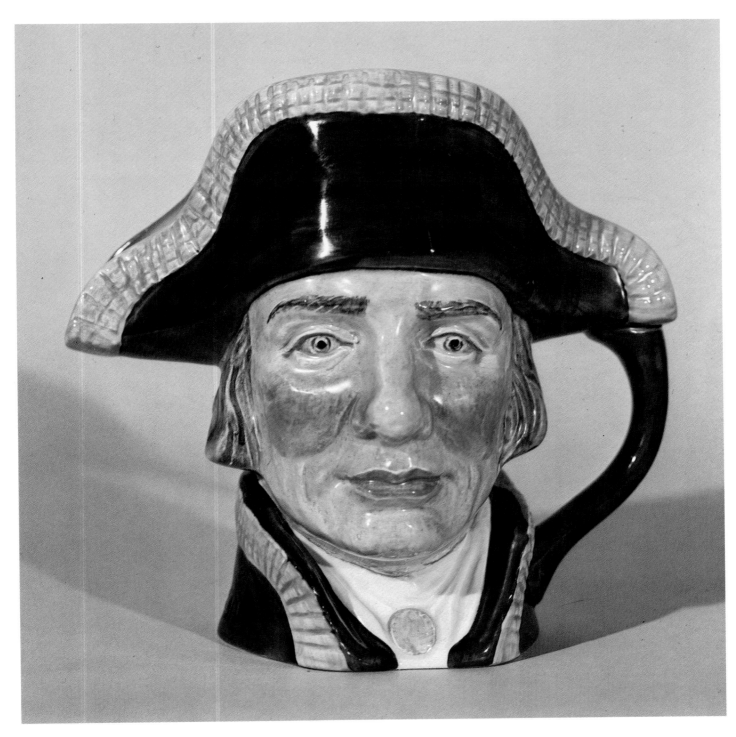

Lord Nelson

Designer: M. Henk
D.6336 (large)
Introduced 1952; withdrawn 1969

Admiral Lord Nelson, one of England's greatest naval heroes, has been a popular subject with ceramic artists and modellers ever since the Battle of Trafalgar, October 1805, during which engagement he received a fatal wound. Early in the nineteenth century Doulton & Watts of Lambeth produced a finely modelled salt-glaze stoneware figure-jug and also a figure-mug in his likeness. These are rare collectors' pieces today as indeed are the replicas made in 1905.

Collectors sometimes ask why the Royal Doulton character jug shows the Admiral without the usual black patch over his right eye. The explanation is very simple. Although Nelson lost the sight of this eye as a result of a wound received during the Battle of Kalvi in 1794, the wound healed without leaving any serious disfigurement. Nelson in fact wore a patch for only a short

period and disliked drawing attention to his disability except on the famous occasion in 1801, when ordered in the Battle of Copenhagen to stop fighting because the British ships were under such heavy fire, he put his telescope to his blind eye and, declaring he saw no such signal, continued the attack, turning what threatened to be a defeat into a victory.

Lumberjack

Designer: M. Henk
D.6610 (large); D.6613 (small)
Introduced 1967; still in production

In 1967 this jug, North American Indian and Trapper were sold exclusively in the North American market, and carried a special backstamp including the words 'Canadian Centennial Series 1867–1967'. The backstamp was eliminated and the jugs issued for world-wide sale in 1968.

The important role played by the lumberjack in the rise and development of the United States and Canada is sometimes overlooked. Lumbering – the logging and sawing of timber – is the oldest industry in both these countries and is still a very large one today, as it is also in Sweden, Finland and the Soviet Union.

Methods vary in different regions. In some parts of Canada, for instance, the logs are cut in the winter and floated down rivers in the spring, when the ice melts, to the sawmills. This may look picturesque but for the lumberjack it is very hard work.

The Doulton lumberjack is shown with his axe which in the early days was his only tool. Since then crosscut saws and, more recently, power saws have made his work somewhat easier. The old settlements of log cabins huddled together have given place to lumbering towns with all modern conveniences.

Mad Hatter

Designer: M. Henk
D.6598 (large); D.6602 (small);
D.6606 (miniature)
Introduced 1965; still in production

A character from Lewis Carroll's *Alice's Adventures in Wonderland* which, since its first appearance in 1865, has continued to delight both adults and children with its strange logic and complex nonsense world.

In her dream Alice follows a White Rabbit down a rabbit-hole and meets many odd characters in an equally odd environment. 'In *that* direction,' said the Cheshire Cat, 'lives a Hatter; and in *that* direction lives a March Hare. Visit either you like; they are both mad!'

The Mad Tea-party which Alice attends with the Hatter, the Hare and a Dormouse is described in one of the most memorable chapters in the book. The Mad Hatter asks Alice a riddle, of the answer to which he later admits he hasn't the slightest idea; he sings a quaint parody of *Twinkle, twinkle, little star*; and has a watch that tells the day of the month but not

'what o'clock it is'! Carroll was a distinguished mathematician and this book and its sequel, *Through the Looking Glass* (1872) contain, in the guise of nonsense, some profound observations on the relativity of time and various philosophical theories.

Mephistopheles

Designers: C. J. Noke and H. Fenton
D.5757 (large); D.5758 (small)
Introduced 1937; withdrawn 1948

Mephistopheles is probably most closely linked in people's minds with the devil to whom Faust sold his soul, in return for his lost youth. The Faust legend, dating back to medieval times (and possibly still earlier) has been the basis of ballads, puppet-plays, books and dramas of which the best known are Marlowe's *The Tragicall History of Dr Faustus* and Goethe's great masterpiece *Faust* to which he devoted many years before completing the final part.

The story of the compact with the Devil is also the subject of a well-known opera by the French composer, Gounod. Liszt wrote a *Faust* symphony and a Mephisto waltz.

The Doulton jug – a rare one nowadays – carries a couplet translated from the French of Rabelais:

'When the devil was sick, the devil a saint
  would be.
When the devil got well, the devil a saint was
  he.'

Appropriately, this is a two-faced jug, showing Mephistopheles in contrasting moods.

This subject was a popular one with Noke, for he also modelled a two-faced figure, *Mephistopheles and Marguerite*, in 1893, and a two-faced match-striker at about the same date.

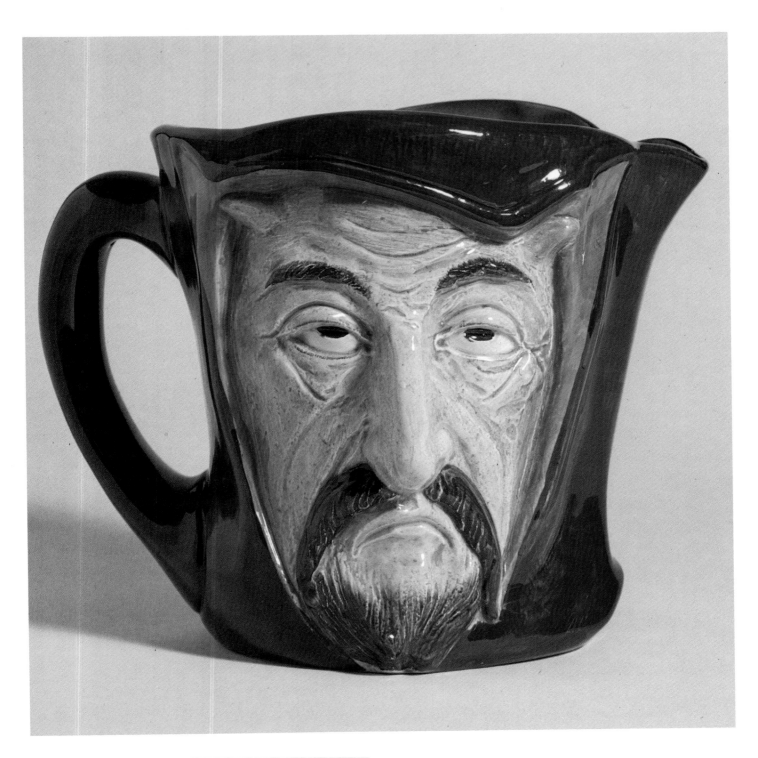

Two-faced *Mephistopheles* match-striker, made
at Burslem during the 1890s.

Merlin

Designer: G. Sharp
D.6529 (large); D.6536 (small);
D.6543 (miniature)
Introduced 1960; still in production

In the old legends and romances narrating the deeds of King Arthur and his Knights of the Round Table, Merlin figures as the wizard and enchanter who works wonders at the Royal Court. It was he who formerly had the charge of the infant King and, at the right time, disclosed to him his royal parentage, thereafter becoming his trusted counsellor.

According to one story, Merlin sprang from the union of a Welsh princess with a demon. He was saved from perdition by Christian baptism but inherited his father's gifts of magic and the ability to foresee the future.

Another story tells how he was beguiled by Vivien, the Lady of the Lake, who entangled him in a thornbush, where he is still sleeping to this day!

The Mikado

Designer: M. Henk
D.6501 (large); D.6507 (small)
Introduced 1959; withdrawn 1969
D.6525 (miniature)
Introduced 1960; withdrawn 1969

'Mikado' is an old Japanese title for Emperor. The word became a familiar one in English-speaking countries because of the tremendous popularity of the Gilbert and Sullivan comic operetta of the same name first produced in 1885.

Since the seventeenth century, Japan had sought to avoid all contact with the West but in 1854 Commodore Perry negotiated a trade treaty which ended Japan's isolation. Growing contacts between East and West led to a tremendous interest in Europe in the late nineteenth century in all things Japanese. It was this fashion for the arts and decorative styles of the Japanese – notably reflected in ceramics – that inspired the theme of the operetta.

Mine Host

Designer: M. Henk
D.6468 (large); D.6470 (small)
Introduced 1958; still in production
D.6513 (miniature)
Introduced 1960; still in production

A jovial, hospitable, sociable character this – one after Sir Toby's own heart, epitomising Old England, good cheer, a festive board and the best brews and vintages. The kind of host the anonymous bard had in mind when he wrote:

> Come, landlord, fill the flowing bowl
> Until it doth run over . . .
> For tonight we'll merry be,
> Tomorrow, we'll be sober

Monty

Designer: H. Fenton
D.6202 (large)
Introduced 1946; still in production
There was a colour change in 1954

Popularly known as 'Monty', Field-Marshal Montgomery (later, Viscount Montgomery of Alamein) served in both World Wars, achieving great distinction in the Second.

Appointed to the command of the badly shaken 8th Army in North Africa, he quickly restored morale and inspired his men with his own determination to win. In October 1942 he launched the successful Battle of Alamein which resulted in the defeat of the German Commander, Rommel – his first serious setback – and the forcing back of the Axis forces to Tunis.

Monty later commanded British Forces taking part in the Allied invasion of Europe.

Mr Micawber

Designers: L. Harradine and
H. Fenton
D.5843 (special size)
Introduced 1938; withdrawn 1948
D.5843 (small size)
Introduced 1948; withdrawn 1960
D.6138 (miniature); D.6143 (tiny)
Introduced 1940; withdrawn 1960
See note under Buz Fuz re scaling
down of original intermediate size

'Micawber, the ever hopeful, the ever-confident, the ever-expectant of something in the turning-up line; with his portentous gentility and his infinite capacity for writing letters.'

This genial but unbusiness-like optimist portrayed in Charles Dickens' *David Copperfield* is in his element sampling his favourite punch. A hostage to fortune, burdened with a wife and several children, constantly out of work and out of funds, he continues to look on the bright side, even in the Fleet Prison.

Mr Micawber is said to have been partly based on Dickens' own father. The word 'Micawberism', derived from this memorable character, is defined in the Oxford Dictionary as the 'policy of trusting that something good will turn up'. A well-known Micawber saying is: 'Annual income twenty pounds, annual expenditure nineteen, nineteen six – result happiness. Annual income twenty pounds, annual expenditure twenty pounds ought and six – result misery.'

Micawber eventually appears in Australia as 'a much esteemed colonial magistrate'.

Mr Pickwick

Designers: L. Harradine and
H. Fenton
D.6060 (large)
Introduced 1940; withdrawn 1960
D.5839 (special size)
Introduced 1938; withdrawn 1948
D.5839 (small size)
Introduced 1948; withdrawn 1960
D.6254 (miniature); D.6260 (tiny)
Introduced 1947; withdrawn 1960
See note under Buz Fuz re scaling
down of original intermediate size

Samuel Pickwick, Founder and General
Chairman of the Pickwick Club, the travels
and odd adventures of whose members
were related by Charles Dickens in the
Posthumous Papers of the Pickwick Club –
generally known simply as the *Pickwick
Papers.*

Pickwick the immortal, the ever young
in heart – despite his bald head and circular
spectacles, despite his amplitude of waistcoat – is brimful of good nature. He can be
very stubborn at times but he has a romantic heart (which sometimes gets him into
trouble) and a disposition positively over-
flowing with the milk of human kindness.

The phrase 'in a Pickwickian sense',
meaning in a merely hypothetical sense, is
derived from an incident in the first
chapter where Mr Blotton says: 'He had
used the word in its Pickwickian sense . . .

He had merely considered him a humbug
in a Pickwickian point of view.'

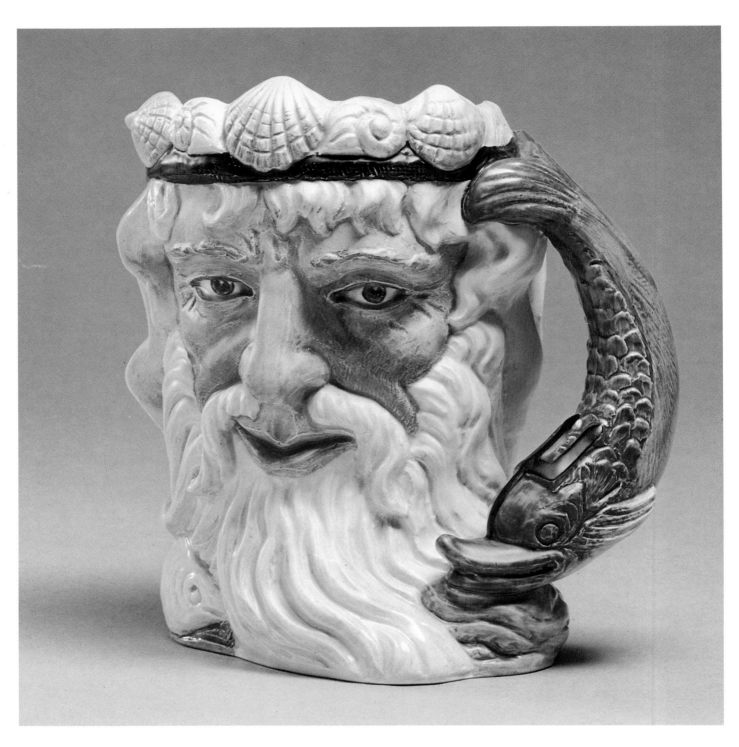

Neptune

Designer: M. Henk
D.6548 (large); D.6552 (small);
D.6555 (miniature)
Introduced 1961; still in production

There are many legends about Neptune whom the Greeks knew as Poseidon. After his father, Saturn (or Cronos) had been deposed, he became god of the seas and rivers. With his wife Amphitrite he dwelt in a golden under-water palace where he kept a team of sea-horses with brazen hooves and golden manes. In his hand he carried his powerful trident and when the sea-horses drew his chariot over the oceans they became tranquil and dolphins played about his path. He was also regarded as the god of storms and earthquakes, the creator of horses and the patron of horse races. One of the planets is named after him.

A light-hearted ceremony 'in honour of Neptune and his wife' is carried out on ships crossing the equator. Those known not to have 'crossed the line' before, are subjected to various rites of 'initiation' which may include being shaved with a big

wooden razor, eating pills made of flour, and being baptised by Neptune in a tub of salt water.

Night Watchman

Designer: M. Henk
D.6569 (large); D.6576 (small);
D.6583 (miniature)
Introduced 1963; still in production
A Character Jug of Williamsburg; see
remarks under Apothecary, page 42

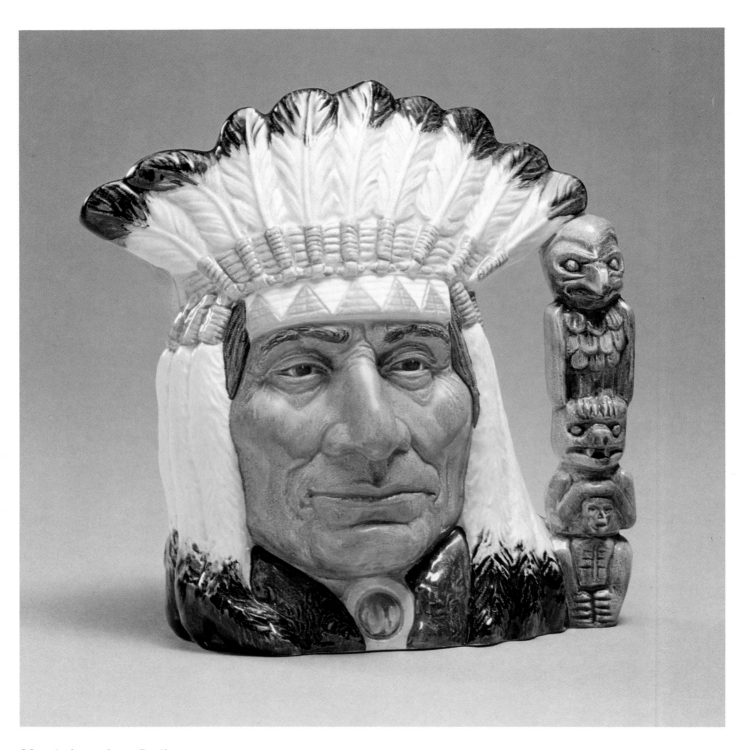

North American Indian

Designer: M. Henk
D.6611 (large); D.6614 (small)
Introduced 1967; still in production
For details of the special backstamp,
see remarks under Lumberjack, page
98

It is believed that the first settlers in North
America may have come from Asia across
the Bering Straits which freeze over in
winter. They included the American
Indians popularly known as 'Red Indians',
– red because of the coppery colour of their
skins and Indians because when
Christopher Columbus reached America
he thought he had arrived in India. There
are several different groups of Indians in
various parts of the United States and
Canada, distinguished not only in
appearance but in language, religious
beliefs and ways of living.

This jug was based on a Chief of the
Blackfoot tribe, and the Feathers in the
headdress denote his position in the tribe,
while the headband includes the yellow
tepee. The modelling of the handle is based
on a Kwakiutl pole at Alert Bay, Vancouver
Island, representing the thunderbird and
bear mother.

Old Charley

Designer: C. J. Noke
D.5420 (large)
Introduced 1934; still in production
D.5527 (small)
Introduced 1935; still in production
D.6046 (miniature)
Introduced 1939; still in production
D.6144 (tiny)
Introduced 1940; withdrawn 1960
Some of the small size have been noted
numbered 5528 in error

The night-watchman of earlier times is
recalled by Old Charley. It was his job –
before a regular police force was created –
to patrol the streets during the night,
calling out the hours and the weather, as for
instance: 'Eleven o'clock of the night; fine
night; all's well.' From Stuart times onwards, a night-watchman was popularly
known as a 'Charley' just as policemen
were later on nicknamed 'Bobbies' – an
allusion to Sir Robert Peel who installed a
police force in London in 1829.
A version of the small-size Old Charley
was produced in 1935 for Bentall's store,
with a special backstamp commemorating
the Royal Jubilee of that year.

Old King Cole

Designer: H. Fenton
D.6036 (large); D.6037 (small)
Introduced 1939; withdrawn 1960
An earlier version with a yellow crown
and other detail differences was piloted
in large and small sizes but probably
did not go into production

Various speculations have been made as to
the identity of this 'Merry Old Soul' of the
well-known nursery rhyme. One theory is
that there was once a real King Cole in
Britain or Ireland, and his name has been
associated with Colchester, the old Roman
town in Essex. There is an ancient tradition which says that St Helen, mother of
the Emperor Constantine the Great, was
King Cole's daughter. A suggestion which
appealed to the novelist, Sir Walter Scott,
was that he was the father of Finn
McCoule, the famous giant in Gaelic
legend. A more prosaic explanation is that
this rhyme was inspired by a merchant
clothier of Reading named Colebrook.

Whatever the truth may be we may
regard him as a symbol of authority, lightly
enjoyed, with an indisputable taste for
wine, tobacco and good music.

Early version of Old King Cole with yellow
crown

Old Salt

Designer: G. Sharp
D.6551 (large); D.6554 (small)
Introduced 1961; still in production
A miniature version was piloted, but
not produced

'One Friday morn as we set sail,
And our ship not far from the land,
We there did espy a fair pretty maid
With a comb and a glass in her hand'

The ship in question sank to the bottom of
the deep blue sea. The Old Salt can spin
hundreds of yarns like this – and even
stranger ones – if given a little liquid
encouragement to remind him of former
days afloat.

Paddy

Designer: H. Fenton
D.5753 (large); D.5768 (small)
Introduced 1937; withdrawn 1960
D.6042 (miniature)
Introduced 1939; withdrawn 1960
D.6145 (tiny)
Introduced 1940; withdrawn 1960
Another version of the miniature,
numbered D.6151 may have been
piloted

Paddy is the familiar form of Padraig or Patrick. St Patrick is the patron saint of Ireland and so many Irish boys are named after him that Paddy has tended to become the nickname of any Irishman whatever.

With his clay pipe in his hat and doubtless, if we could see it, his shillelagh under his arm, the roguish-looking character depicted by Harry Fenton recalls a type once familiar in old songs, ballads and popular music-hall sketches and stories but long since vanished, if indeed he ever existed.

Parson Brown

Designer: C. J. Noke
D.5486 (large); D.5529 (small)
Introduced 1935; withdrawn 1960

Parson Brown recalls a typical sporting
Anglican parson of the eighteenth and
nineteenth centuries, who liked to roam his
scattered parish on horseback and was
always ready to take a drink or lay a small
wager with the local squire over the result
of a steeplechase or a bout of fisticuffs.

The Pied Piper

Designer: M. Henk
D.6403 (large)
Introduced 1954; still in production
D.6462 (small)
Introduced in 1957; still in production
D.6514 (miniature)
Introduced 1960; still in production

A figure of medieval legend, the Pied Piper of Hamelin was immortalised in English verse by Robert Browning. He is also the subject of several German poems of which the best known is *Der Rattenfänger* by Julius Wolff.

One version of the legend suggests that the children who were led away by the piper did not perish in the mountains but were guided into Transylvania, where they founded a German colony.

In Browning's poem the more traditional story is followed. Hamelin is infested by rats and nobody knows how to deal with them until the Pied Piper with 'his queer long coat from heel to head . . . half of yellow and half of red' arrives on the scene and offers, for an agreed fee, to charm them away by his piping. This he does successfully but when he asks for the fee he is offered only a mere fraction of it. There-

upon he began to pipe again; 'out came the children running' and followed him to a hill where a cave opened and all were swallowed up, save a lame boy who arrived too late.

Poacher

Designer: M. Henk
D.6429 (large)
Introduced 1955; still in production
D.6464 (small)
Introduced 1957; still in production
D.6515 (miniature)
Introduced 1960; still in production

Poachers – that is to say, trespassers on private property in quest of fish or game – have been following their 'pursuits' for thousands of years and, despite often severe penalties if caught, are still at it today.

The character depicted by the Royal Doulton Jug looks astute but harmless and friendly for all that. Probably by day he follows some quite ordinary and respected calling; only under cover of darkness does he become a poacher. Salmon and trout are among his most prized quarries. 'Tickling a trout' is an art he has brought to great perfection. He wades quietly into the stream, inducing the fish under a bank; then gently stroking its sides he persuades it to stay still until, in a flash, he can seize it firmly by the gills.

Porthos

Designer: M. Henk
D.6440 (large); D.6453 (small)
Introduced 1956; still in production
D.6516 (miniature)
Introduced 1960; still in production
See remarks under Aramis, page 43

Punch and Judy Man

Designer: D. Biggs
D.6590 (large); D.6593 (small);
D.6596 (miniature)
Introduced 1964; withdrawn 1969

Although nobody quite knows how they began, Punch and Judy shows, more or less as we know them, became immensely popular throughout the long reign of Queen Victoria and have delighted successive generations of children ever since, when performed at fairs and similar entertainments or on seaside beaches and piers.

In the eighteenth century, fashionable people are said to have crowded the theatre in Covent Garden, London, to see puppet shows in which, among other characters, there appeared as a commentator a wooden figure, named Punch, worked by wires. His wife's name was then Joan and the performance was quite different from that of the contemporary glove puppets.

A rogue named Pulcinello took a prominent part in Italian and French plays of the sixteenth and seventeenth centuries. He was adopted as a hero by puppet showmen and may be regarded as the ancestor of our present-day Punch.

Regency Beau

Designer: D. Biggs
D.6559 (large); D.6562 (small);
D.6565 (miniature)
Introduced 1962; withdrawn 1967

The 'beaux' who flourished, especially in London, Brighton and Bath, during the period when the future George IV had become notorious as the pleasure-seeking Prince Regent, were wealthy men of fashion who devoted much of their time to dressing and living elegantly.

Best known of them all was Beau Brummell (1778–1840) whose style in dress was so admired that some of his most fashionable contemporaries took his advice about what they should wear. George himself – the first gentleman of Europe, as he was called – is said to have burst into tears when told that Brummell did not approve of a coat he was wearing!

Rip Van Winkle

Designer: M. Henk
D.6438 (large)
Introduced 1955; still in production
D.6463 (small)
Introduced 1957; still in production
D.6517 (miniature)
Introduced 1960; still in production

Rip Van Winkle is a character in one of the stories in Washington Irving's *Sketch Book* (published 1819). Irving based the story on an old legend told by Dutch settlers in New York Province about a man who went to sleep and only awakened many years later. To give it credence he pretended he had found it among the posthumous papers of an imaginary Diedrich Knickerbocker, the chief merit of whose literary work was 'its scrupulous accuracy'.

In 1920 Percy MacKaye wrote the libretto and Reginald de Koven the music for a folk opera *Rip Van Winkle*.

Robin Hood (first version)

Designer: H. Fenton
D.6205 (large); D.6234 (small);
D.6252 (miniature)
Introduced 1947; withdrawn 1960

Robin Hood (second version)

Designer: M. Henk
D.6527 (large); D.6534 (small);
D.6541 (miniature)
Introduced 1960; still in production
This is an entirely different model
from the first version. Robin now has
oak leaves and acorns in his hat and the
handle is also different

The romantic outlaw hero of many old
ballads, Robin Hood – who robbed the rich
to feed the poor – is mentioned in print for
the first time in Langland's *Vision of Piers
Plowman*, published in 1377. The first
published collection of ballads, narrating
his legendary exploits, was the *Lytel Geste
of Robin Hood*, printed by Wynkyn de
Worde, c.1492–1510.

The Robin Hood legend probably had
some historical basis and is an interesting
expression of the popular mind about the
end of the Middle Ages. Robin may be said
to represent the ideal yeoman just as
Arthur in an earlier epoch, symbolised the
ideal of kingly chivalry.

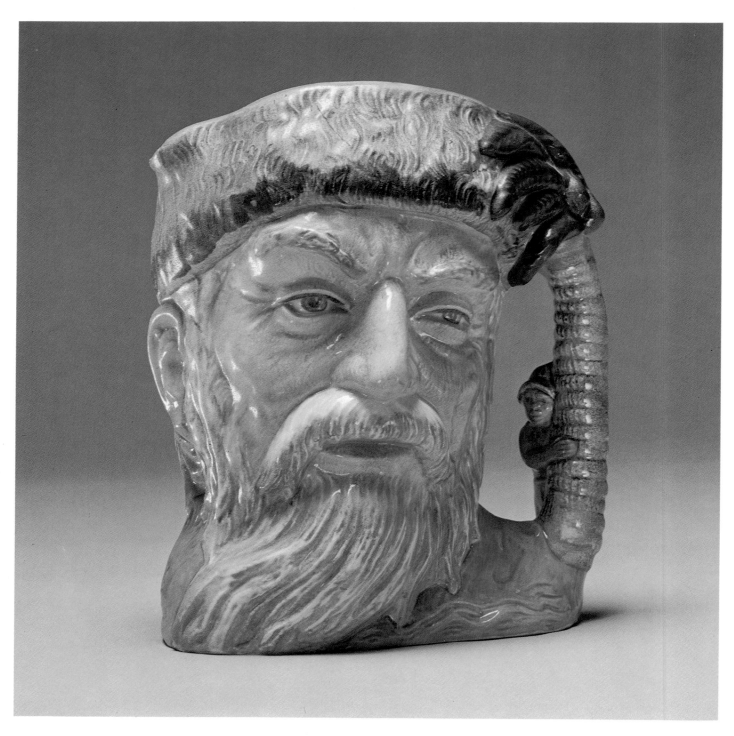

Robinson Crusoe

Designer: M. Henk
D.6532 (large); D.6539 (small);
D.6546 (miniature)
Introduced 1960; still in production

Daniel Defoe's tale of the unusual adventures of *Robinson Crusoe* proved an instant 'best-seller' and has since appeared again and again in many editions and several languages. Based partly on the true story of one Alexander Selkirk, who was shipwrecked on the desert island of Juan Fernandez, it tells with much realistic detail how Crusoe managed to cope with his solitary existence, building a cabin and a boat, domesticating goats, and keeping both body and mind generally active.

One of the most exciting parts of the story describes Crusoe's consternation at the visit of some savage cannibals and his rescue of 'Man Friday' from death.

St George

Designer: M. Henk
D.6618 (large); D.6621 (small)
Introduced 1968; withdrawn 1975

In an old legend, first related in England by crusaders returning from Palestine, St George is said to have saved from certain death a King's daughter, the lovely Melisande, by slaying a fearful fire-breathing dragon that ravaged the land and demanded a daily human sacrifice.

Little or nothing is known about the real St George. One version is that he lived somewhere in Asia Minor and was martyred by the Emperor Diocletian in AD 303

Edward III adopted him as patron saint of England and patron of the Order of the Garter but already in the reign of Richard I St George's banner – a red cross on a white ground –was a heraldic device. It now forms part of the Union Jack, the national flag of Great Britain and Northern Ireland.

Sairey Gamp

Designers: L. Harradine and
H. Fenton
D.5451 (large); D.5528 (small)
Introduced 1935; still in production
D.6045 (miniature)
Introduced 1939; still in production
D.6146 (tiny)
Introduced 1940; withdrawn 1960

Sairey Gamp, the bibulous, garrulous midwife and sick-nurse from *The Life and
Adventures of Martin Chuzzlewit* is one of
Charles Dicken's best-known characters.
She is described as 'a fat old woman . . .
with a husky voice and a moist eye which
she had a remarkable power of turning up
and only showing the white of it . . . It was
difficult to enjoy her society without
becoming conscious of a smell of spirits'.
She invariably carried an umbrella and
thereby has added the word 'gamp' to the
English language.

Writing about Sairey twenty-four years
after the publication of the novel, Dickens
said 'She was a fair representation of the
hired attendant on the poor in sickness'.

Samuel Johnson

Designer: H. Fenton
D.6289 (large); D.6296 (small)
Introduced 1950; withdrawn 1960

The great English writer and lexicographer, Samuel Johnson, is probably best
remembered today for his brilliant
conversation as recorded by James Boswell
and others. Johnson was born at Lichfield
in Staffordshire in 1709. He studied for a
time at Pembroke College, Oxford, but left
without a degree for lack of money. He
opened an Academy for students in 1735
but apparently only obtained three – one of
them David Garrick, later manager of
Drury Lane Theatre. In 1747 Johnson
began his great work, a *Dictionary of the
English Language*, which he completed
seven years later.

He declared late in life that he thought a
day lost in which he did not make a new
acquaintance. He took a great delight in
frequenting taverns and clubs and attracted
many friends. It has been said that no man
ever had a more distinguished or numerous
circle around him.

One of Johnson's many famous remarks
was 'When a man is tired of London, he is
tired of life; for there is in London all that
life can afford'.

Sam Weller

Designers: L. Harradine and
H. Fenton
D.6064 (large)
Introduced 1940; withdrawn 1960
D.5841 (special size)
Introduced 1938; withdrawn 1948
D.5841 (small size)
Introduced 1948; withdrawn 1960
D.6140 (miniature); D.6147 (tiny)
Introduced 1940; withdrawn 1960
See note under Buz Fuz for scaling
down of original intermediate size

Another memorable character from
Dickens' *Pickwick Papers* Sam Weller was
formerly boots at the 'White Hart' in the
Borough before leaving to become Mr
Pickwick's devoted manservant and
'gen'l'm'n's gen'l'm'n'. A cheerful,
facetious and resourceful character, he is
the immortal type of humorous,
shrewd-witted, good-natured Cockney.
Sam has, in his master's own words 'A
considerable knowledge of the world and a
great deal of sharpness'.

Sam is not averse to 'except of half a
guinea' and is always at hand to look after
Mr Pickwick in every vicissitude and to
help extricate him from the scrapes in
which he often innocently involves himself.

Many critics regard Sam Weller as the
greatest character that Dickens ever drew.

Sancho Panza

Designer: G. Blower
D.6456 (large); D.6461 (small)
Introduced 1957; still in production
D.6518 (miniature)
Introduced 1960; still in production
See remarks under Don Quixote, page
67

Scaramouche

Designer: M. Henk
D.6558 (large); D.6561 (small);
D.6564 (miniature)
Introduced 1962; withdrawn 1967

A buffoon in motley dress, notorious for his bragging and cowardice, Scaramouche was originally a character in the Italian *Commedia del' Arte*.

He was featured in a novel of the same name by Rafael Sabbatini which was later dramatised and had a long run in London's West End during the 1920s.

Simon the Cellarer

Designers: C. J. Noke and H. Fenton
D.5504 (large)
Introduced 1935; withdrawn 1960
D.5616 (small)
Introduced 1936; withdrawn 1960

Depicted with his bundle of keys, Simon is the wine-cellarer immortalised in a popular nineteenth-century drinking song by W. H. Bellamy. He had in his charge a rare store of Malmsey, Malvoisie, Cyprus and other wines, in the tasting of which he was an expert of high order and much capacity.

He is shown in Elizabethan costume and no doubt Sir Toby Belch would have appreciated his companionship.

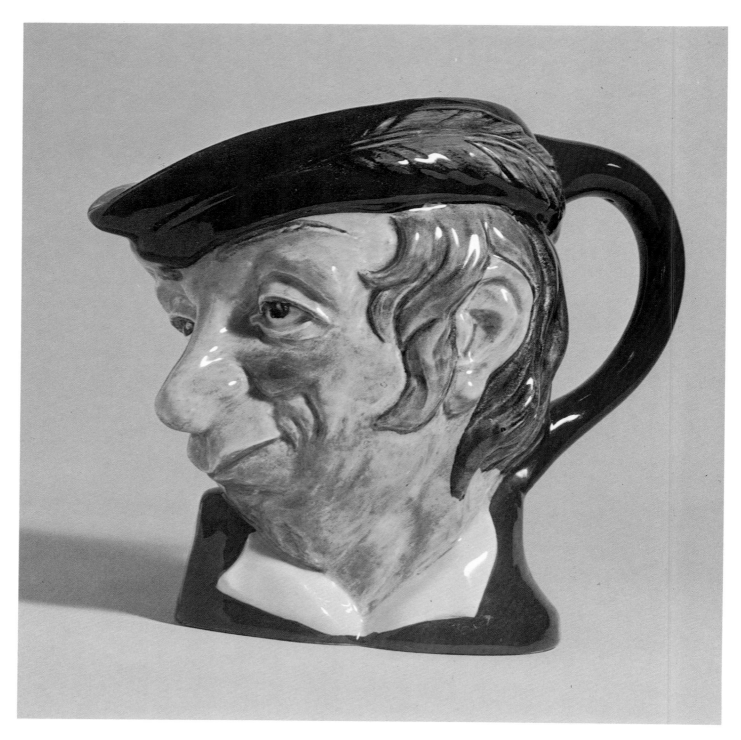

Simple Simon

Designer: M. Henk
D.6374 (large)
Introduced 1953; withdrawn 1960

Ballads and chapbook tales of Simple
Simon, a character in a much-loved
children's nursery rhyme, date back to the
seventeenth century. It has been suggested
that Simon was a generic nickname in
medieval times for a 'natural' or 'silly
fellow'.

Sleuth

Designer: A. Moore
D.6631 (large); D.6635 (small);
D.6639 (miniature)
Introduced 1973; still in production

This jug was inspired by Sir Arthur Conan Doyle's famous private detective, Sherlock Holmes, who is always assuring his stolid friend, foil and chronicler, Dr Watson, that all his most abstruse deductions are 'Elementary, my dear Watson'.

The term 'sleuth', much used in popular fiction to denote a detective, is derived from an old Norse word 'sloth' meaning a track. A slot-hound or sleuth-hound is thus a hound which tracks its prey by the scent.

Smuggler

Designer: D. Biggs
D.6616 (large); D.6619 (small)
Introduced 1968; still in production

'Them that asks no questions isn't told a lie.
Watch the wall, my darling, while the
gentlemen go by!
Five and twenty ponies
Trotting through the dark –
Brandy for the Parson,
'Baccy for the Clerk;
Laces for a lady, letters for a spy,
Watch the wall, my darling, while the
gentlemen go by!'

'The Gentlemen' in Rudyard Kipling's
A Smuggler's Song are of course
importing goods under cover of
darkness to avoid paying duty on them.
Some romantic and amusing stories
have been told about smugglers and
even some parsons, magistrates and
country gentlemen in the eighteenth
century dabbled in smuggling or
accepted smuggled goods. There were

also grim tales of gangs of smugglers
who inspired fear and dread among
dwellers near the coasts.

Smuts

Designer: H. Fenton
D.6198 (large)
Introduced 1946; withdrawn c.1948

Jan Christian Smuts (1870–1950), the great South African statesman, was the son of a Boer farmer. He studied law at Cambridge University but in the Boer War against Great Britain he fought as a guerilla and led a daring raid into the Cape Colony in 1901.

After the war, Smuts bore no grudge but tried to promote good feeling between the various racial groups in the Union of South Africa. Throughout World War I he continued to work for Anglo-Boer co-operation and again during World War II he supported Britain and the Allies, despite great opposition from other South African statesmen.

He took a leading part in founding both the League of Nations and the United Nations. A keen mountaineer, he regularly climbed Table Mountain even in his late seventies.

On the base of the Doulton jug is inscribed.
FIELD MARSHAL THE RIGHT HONOURABLE
J. C. SMUTS, KC, CH, DTD
PRIME MINISTER OF THE UNION OF
SOUTH AFRICA AND COMMANDER IN
CHIEF OF SOUTH AFRICAN FORCES

Tam O'Shanter

Designer: M. Henk
D.6632 (large); D.6636 (small);
D.6640 (miniature)
Introduced 1973; still in production

Tam O'Shanter is a farmer vividly portrayed in Robert Burns' poem of the same name published in 1790.

Returning from Ayr one night, the worse for liquor, he sees the Kirk of Alloway all lit up. Stopping to investigate, he finds a whole coven of witches and warlocks dancing to tunes played on the bagpipes by Old Nick himself. He is attracted by one of the prettiest of the witches, 'a winsome wench', and calls out 'Weel done, Cutty Sark!' (Cutty Sark is Scots for 'Short Chemise').

The lights go out and the witches make for Tam like a swarm of furious bees. Spurring on his grey mare, Meg, he manages to reach the middle of the bridge over the Doon before the 'Cutty Sark' catches him. He is now out of her power but Meg's tail is still within her territory and this she pulls off.

Toby Philpots

Designer: C. J. Noke
D.5736 (large); D.5737 (small)
Introduced 1937; withdrawn 1969
D.6043 (miniature)
Introduced 1939; withdrawn 1969
See pages 17–21 for details about the
origin of the name Toby Fillpot

Tony Weller

Designers: L. Harradine and
H. Fenton
D.5531 (large); D.5530 (small)
Introduced 1936; withdrawn 1960
D.6044 (miniature)
Introduced 1939; withdrawn 1960
An extra large version of this jug was
also produced

Tony Weller, a coach driver, is the father
of Sam Weller.

Out of a mature experience of life he has
become a meditative philosopher of sorts, a
firm believer in the virtue and power of a
'haliby' and a convinced mistruster of
'vidders'.

Touchstone

Designer: C. J. Noke
D.5613 (large)
Introduced 1936; withdrawn 1960

Touchstone is the clown in Shakespeare's
As You Like It who shoots his wit under
the guise of folly. He accompanies Celia
and Rosalind on their adventures in the
Forest of Arden and makes 'Many a clever
jest e'en when his heart is sore'.

'He is a rare fellow', wrote William
Hazlitt, the essayist. 'He is a mixture of the
ancient cynic philosopher with the modern
buffoon, and turns folly into wit, and wit
into folly, just as the fit takes him.'

Town Crier

Designer: D. Biggs
D.6530 (large); D.6537 (small);
D.6544 (miniature)
Introduced 1960; withdrawn 1973

For centuries before the coming of news-
papers it was the Town Crier in his cocked
hat and resplendent uniform who made
known to the townspeople important hap-
penings, forthcoming events, announce-
ments of meetings, details of strayed
animals, articles lost and found, and the
like.

He would ring a bell to attract attention
and precede his proclamations by repeating
three times in a loud voice 'Oyez! Oyez!
Oyez!' – oyez being the old Norman
French for 'hear ye'.

Trapper

Designers: M. Henk and D. Biggs
D.6609 (large); D.6612 (small)
Introduced 1967; still in production
A miniature version was piloted but not
produced
For details of the special backstamp,
see remarks under Lumberjack, page
98

A jug representing Buffalo Bill was piloted
c.1965 but not produced. The Trapper,
however, is partly based on it.

Trapping – the art of capturing or
killing animals by means of traps – has
been practised since prehistoric times; the
earliest traps probably being simple pitfalls
as still used by primitive peoples.

The trapping of animals for their furs or
pelts, rather than for food, is practised on a
large scale in North America and the
northern parts of the USSR. A famous
early trapper was Davy Crockett of
Tennessee who has become a children's
hero, especially in America.

During Canada's early history, furs
were a principal article of commerce. It was
the attractive possibilities of the fur trade
that led to the founding of Quebec by
Champlain in 1608, followed by further
exploration and the opening up of the
interior.

The life of the early trappers in America
was a hard one. Their great enemies were
wolves and bears, the extremes of weather,
and the native Indians.

The need for trapping has nowadays
been greatly reduced since fur-bearing
animals are being bred on special farms.

Ugly Duchess

Designer: M. Henk
D.6599 (large); D.6603 (small);
D.6607 (miniature)
Introduced 1965; withdrawn 1973

Another of Lewis Carroll's dream-world characters in *Alice in Wonderland*, the Ugly Duchess is a moralising, violent virago. 'Take care of the sense and the sounds will take care of themselves,' she tells Alice. Other remarks of hers are: 'If everybody minded their own business, the world would go round a deal faster than it does', and 'The more there is of mine, the less there is of yours'.

Alice first meets her in the smoky pepper-filled kitchen where she is sitting on a three-legged stool nursing on her knee an odd kind of baby which she keeps tossing violently up and down. Later on, at the King and Queen of Hearts' croquet ground, where the players use flamingoes as mallets and hedge-hogs as balls, the Duchess boxes the Queen's ears and is sentenced to have her head chopped off. The penalty for her ill-tempered treason is subsequently reduced to banishment.

Uncle Tom Cobbleigh

Designer: M. Henk
D.6337 (large)
Introduced 1952; withdrawn 1960

One of the characters in a well-known song in which 'Uncle Tom Cobbleigh and all' rode on a single horse to Widdecombe Fair. Widdecombe is in Devonshire and the song dates from about 1800.

One of the verses goes as follows:
'Tom Pearse, Tom Pearse, lend me your grey mare,
All along, down along, out along, lee,
For I want for to go to Widdicombe Fair
Wi'Bill Brewer, Jan Stewer, Peter Gurney,
Peter Davey, Dan'l Whiddon, Harry Hawk,
Old Uncle Tom Cobbleigh and all
Old Uncle Tom Cobbleigh and all.

In a church in Widdicombe there is a tomb which bears the inscription: 'Thomas Cobley, age 96, 6th March 1794.' If he be the original of Uncle Tom it is not clear how he came to be associated with the song.

Veteran Motorist

Designer: D. Biggs
D.6633 (large); D.6637 (small);
D.6641 (miniature)
Introduced 1973; still in production

Each year, in November, the Veteran Car Run is held, from London to Brighton. Many magnificently preserved and restored vehicles are entered for the rally, all of which have to have been manufactured before 1905. The rally commemorates the abolition of the early law which decreed that all self-propelled vehicles had to be preceded by a man carrying a red flag.

The cars, driven by their enthusiast owners, many of whom dress in the motoring costume of the period, as depicted on this jug, have to complete the journey within a certain time. The event always attracts large crowds who share the owners' fascination for these early road vehicles.

The Vicar of Bray

Designer: C. J. Noke and H. Fenton
D.5615 (large)
Introduced 1936; withdrawn 1960

'And this is law, I will maintain
Unto my dying day, Sir,
That whatsoever King shall reign
I will be the Vicar of Bray, Sir!'

It is popularly assumed that the sail-trimming Vicar was an incumbent of the little parish of that name on the right bank of the Thames, near Maidenhead in Berkshire. The song is traditionally ascribed to the reign of George I in the eighteenth century.

Some authorities think the song was inspired by another parson, Simon Aleyn, who is said to have been twice a Roman Catholic and twice a Protestant during the successive reigns of Henry VIII, Edward VI, Mary and Elizabeth I.

No doubt other clergy went through similar changes of front during the equally changeable religious climates of Charles I, Oliver Cromwell, Charles II, James II and William and Mary.

Viking

Designer: M. Henk
D.6496 (large); D.6502 (small)
Introduced 1959; withdrawn 1975
D.6526 (miniature)
Introduced 1960; withdrawn 1975

The Vikings were piratical Scandinavian seafarers and explorers who, between the eighth and eleventh centuries particularly, inspired fear and terror wherever they went. It is not surprising that their fast skilfully built long-ships with their fire-breathing dragon figureheads have become the symbol of their might.

These fair-haired fierce warriors came first to plunder but later to trade and establish settlements in, among other places, Scotland, England, Ireland, Normandy, Finland, Greenland, Poland and Russia. Some of their raids reached south to the Mediterranean and centuries before Columbus' rediscovery they had reached the shores of the North American continent, probably between Nova Scotia and Cape Cod.

They are reputed to have indulged excessively at times in alchoholic feasts and celebrations, at which vast quantities of beer, mead and stolen or traded wine would be consumed as well as various potent brews made from fruits and plants.

146

Walrus and Carpenter

Designer: M. Henk
D.6600 (large); D.6604 (small);
D.6608 (miniature)
Introduced 1965; still in production

In *Through the Looking-Glass*, another Lewis Carroll classic, Alice walks in a reverie through the large mirror into Looking-Glass House, where she finds the Red and White Kings and Queens and other chess-pieces all alive, walks through the garden of live flowers and meets Humpty Dumpty, Tweedledum and Tweedledee and other strange characters.

Tweedledee recites for her a very long poem about the Walrus and the Carpenter. Of the eighteen verses, the following is one of the most often quoted:

'The time has come', the Walrus said,
'To talk of many things:
Of shoes – and ships – and sealing-wax –
Of cabbages – and Kings –
And why the sea is boiling hot –
And whether pigs have wings.'

Yachtsman

Designer: D. Biggs
D.6622 (large)
Introduced 1971; still in production
A small and a miniature version were
piloted but not produced

A traditional part of England's history has been fascination with the sea. Perhaps inevitable in an island race, this fascination has produced a great number of famous sailors. In the past Raleigh, Drake, Cook, Nelson and others carried the English flag across the oceans of the world. More recently the English have turned their attention to small boats. Sailing has become a national pastime, with weekend sailors galore filling every creek and clubhouse. There have also been a number of impressive feats of individual seamanship, the most important of which was Sir Francis Chichester's single-handed sail around the world, an event which perhaps inspired this jug.

Toby Jugs

Sairey Gamp   Mr Micawber   Mr Pickwick   The Fat Boy   Sam Weller   Cap'n Cuttle

Old Charley   The Squire   Double XX   The Best is not too Good

Falstaff

Happy John

Honest Measure

The Best is Not Too Good

Designer: H. Fenton
D.6107, 4½ in (11·4 cm) high
Introduced 1939; withdrawn 1960

Depicts a jovial connoisseur of fine brews whose ambition was 'Old wood to burn, old ale to drink, and old friends to trust'.

Cap'n Cuttle

Designer: H. Fenton
D.6266, 4½ in (11·4 cm)
Introduced 1948; withdrawn 1960

Double XX or the Man on the Barrel

Designer: H. Fenton
D.6088, 6½ in (16·5 cm)
Introduced 1939; withdrawn 1969

This jug aptly portrays Toby's ambition to sit astride a barrel of extra strong brew and find an excuse for yet another mug of ale.

Falstaff

Designer: C. J. Noke
D.6062, 8½ in (21·5 cm); D.6063, 5¼ in (13·3 cm)
Introduced 1939; still in production
See also page 70

The Doulton catalogue for 1976 mentioned a miniature size in error.

The Fat Boy

Designer: H. Fenton
D.6264, 4½ in (11·4 cm)
Introduced 1948; withdrawn 1960
See also page 72

Happy John

Designer: H. Fenton
D.6031, 9 in (22·8 cm); D.6070, 5½ in (13·9 cm)
Introduced 1939; still in production

This jug and the one depicting 'Old Charley' have something in common with the eighteenth-century Tobies; they also owe something to the stoneware jugs designed by Harry Simeon at Lambeth in the 1920s and 1930s.

Honest Measure

Designer: H. Fenton
D.6108, 4½ in (11·4 cm)
Introduced 1939; still in production

'Honest Measure: Drink at Leisure' runs the inscription on this jug and Toby evidently intends to live up to it.

The Huntsman

Designer: H. Fenton
D.6320, 7½ in (19 cm)
Introduced 1950; still in production

Loves the gallop and his sturdy hunter; knows his pack by name and smacks his top boots with his crop to emphasise his opinions.
See also page 80

The Huntsman

Jolly Toby

Sir Winston Churchill

Jolly Toby

Designer: H. Fenton
D.6109, 6½ in (15·8 cm)
Introduced 1939; still in production

With his warm smile, reclining at ease, Jolly Toby is evidently living up to his name.

Mr Micawber

Designer: H. Fenton
D.6262, 4½ in (11·4 cm)
Introduced 1948; withdrawn 1960
See also page 106

Mr Pickwick

Designer: H. Fenton
D.6261, 4½ in (11·4 cm)
Introduced 1948, withdrawn 1960
See also page 107

Old Charley

Designer: H. Fenton
D.6030, 8¾ in (22·2 cm); D.6069, 5½ in (13·9 cn)
Introduced 1939; withdrawn 1960
See also page 111

Sairey Gamp

Designer: H. Fenton
D.6263, 4½ in (11·4 cm)
Introduced 1948; withdrawn 1960
See also page 126

Sam Weller

Designer: H. Fenton
D.6265, 4½ in (11·4 cm)
Introduced 1948; withdrawn 1960
See also page 128

The Squire

Designer: H. Fenton
D.6319, 6 in (15·2 cm)
Introduced 1950; withdrawn 1969

In early medieval times the squire was an assistant to a knight, whom he served at table, whose weapons he carried, and whom he accompanied into battle. By the thirteenth century the designation was applied to young men of good family training in noble households to become knights themselves.

Yet another change in the meaning of the word came in the seventeenth century when the descendants of earlier knights and squires became wealthy and important landowners. These local squires, as they were now called, more or less controlled local affairs and played a sometimes benevolent, sometimes dictatorial part in the lives of the villagers in their domain.

The title 'esquire' remains as a reminder of the squirearchy but that too is becoming practically obsolete.

Sir Winston Churchill

Designer: H. Fenton
D.6171, 9 in (22·8 cm); D.6172, 5½ in (13·9 cm); D.6175, 4 in (10·1 cm)
Introduced 1941; still in production

A much more satisfactory model than the jug illustrated on page 62, this Toby was described at the time as a tribute to 'the greatest and most admired Englishman of the century. An incomparable leader; master of our language whether spoken or written, his magnanimity is an inspiration to our Age. Beloved by free peoples, feared by tyrants, symbol for Anglo-American friendship!' Early models were inscribed on the base, Winston Churchill Prime Minister of Great Britain 1940.

Rare Piloted Character Jugs

Illustrated below are a number of rare piloted jugs that never went into production. These have been included because examples are reported from time to time by collectors.

The Maori

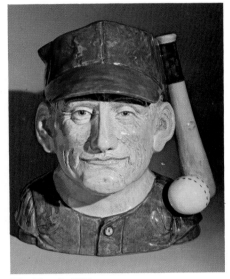

The Baseball Player

Buffalo Bill

Two versions of the Maori and the photograph upon which one was based

McCallum Character Jug

A slip-painted Kingsware character jug representing a Highlander was made for the whisky distillers, D. & J. McCallum in the early 1930s. About 1,000 of these jugs are thought to have been produced, all painted in the typical sombre Kingsware colours

Charrington Toby

For some years from about 1954 onwards large-size Toby Jugs (9¼ in, 18·8 cm) were supplied to Charrington, the well-known brewers, for advertising purposes. These were made in at least two versions, one inscribed TOBY ALES and the other ONE TOBY LEADS TO ANOTHER.

Left: The McCallum Character Jug

Right: The two versions of the Charrington Toby

The George Robey Jug

Hoare Toby Jug

A jug modelled as a seated toper is recorded as having been made during the early 1930s to advertise this ale. No other details are available.

It is possible that other seated Toby Jugs were used by brewers for advertising purposes.

George Robey Jug

About 1910 some amusing covered jugs ($10\frac{1}{2}$ in, 26·6 cm high) were made to special order representing the famous English music hall artist. He wears a crumpled suit, his flat hat forms the cover and his face bears a typical expression. The quantity made is not recorded, but it cannot have been very large. However, it appears to have been still in production during the 1920s.

It is possible that a similar Charlie Chaplin jug was produced.

Cliff Cornell Jugs

In 1956 special Toby Jugs were produced for Cliff Cornell, an American industrialist, for presentation to friends and business associates. The bases carry the inscription: GREETINGS   CLIFF CORNELL   FAMOUS CORNELL FLUXES CLEVELAND FLUX COMPANY

The quantity made was approximately 1,750, made up as follows:
500 large size (9 in, 18·3 cm), with brown suit
500 large size (9 in, 18·3 cm), with blue suit
375 medium size ($5\frac{1}{2}$ in, 13·9 cm), with brown suit
375 medium size ($5\frac{1}{2}$ in, 13·9 cm), with blue suit

The exact number is not known because Doulton stipulated that Mr Cornell had to accept 5% above or below the quantity ordered to allow for the inevitable losses during firing and decoration.

A few prototypes of a small size were also submitted to Mr Cornell, but this size was not ordered.

Many collectors have commented on the likeness between the Cornell and Winston Churchill Toby Jugs. It seems that Mr Cornell greatly admired Churchill and so asked for his jugs to be modelled in similar style.

The four versions of the Cliff Cornell Jug

Prototype John Wesley Toby Jug.
No other details are recorded

Character whisky flasks in the form of a
Scotsman and an Irishman, with
detachable heads. These were specially
made for Asprey & Co. during the 1930s,
and were designed by H. Fenton

Dickens Jugs and Tankards

Six rectangular jugs and a round tankard, all decorated in low relief with
characters and scenes from Dickens, were illustrated in *Collectors' Book No. 3*,
produced by Doulton in the early 1950s.

Although not strictly related to the Character and Toby Jugs with which that
booklet was primarily concerned, it appears that many collectors now consider
these items to be part of the Character and Toby Jug range. Details of these are
therefore listed below. Many other jugs and loving cups decorated in this low
relief style of modelling were produced by Royal Doulton. Information about
these is included in *The Doulton Burslem Wares*, by Desmond Eyles to be
published by Hutchinson in 1980

Old London Jug, D.6291
London in Dickens' day, with Old Charley on one side and Sairey Gamp on the
other

Peggotty Jug, D.6292
A scene from *David Copperfield*

Old Curiosity Shop Jug, D.5584
Little Nell and her grandfather on one side, the Marchioness on the other

Pickwick Papers Jug, D.5756
Mr Pickwick, Sam Weller, Tony Weller and the Fat Boy outside the White Hart
Inn

Oliver Twist Jug, D.5617
Oliver, the Artful Dodger, Fagin and Bumble

Oliver Twist Jug, D.6285
Oliver asking for more

Oliver Twist Tankard, D.6286
Oliver watching the Artful Dodger picking a pocket

The Old Curiosity Shop Jug was introduced in 1935, the first Oliver Twist Jug in
1936, the Pickwick Papers Jug in 1937 and the others in 1949. All were withdrawn
in 1960.

Pickwick Papers Jug   Peggotty Jug
    Old London Jug   Oliver Twist Tankard Oliver Twist Jug

Old Curiosity Shop Jug
        Oliver Asks for More Jug

Miscellaneous Wares

In addition to the Character Jugs and Toby Jugs listed and described on earlier pages, the Royal Doulton Potteries also produced a variety of other wares featuring some of the personalities already depicted by the jugs.

Such items derived from Character and Toby Jugs have always aroused considerable interest among collectors. The following list has been prepared from a number of sources and private collections in Britain and North America and so is hopefully as complete as possible. However, both Royal Doulton and the author of this book would be pleased to hear of any other variants that come to light.

Most, if not all, of these items were designed by H. Fenton.

Tony Weller Musical Jug, and detail of a base showing the mechanism

Old Charley tobacco jar

Musical Jugs

Between the end of 1937 and c. 1948 a number of Character Jugs were produced with an extended base and the addition of a mechanism which played a tune appropriate to the Character. The quantities involved were comparatively small and so these jugs are now quite rare..

Here is a list of the jugs and the tunes which went with them:

D.5858, Old Charley: *Here's a health unto His Majesty*
D.5887, Paddy: *Irish Jig*
D.5888, Tony Weller: *Come, Landlord, fill the flowing bowl*
D.5889, Owd Mac: *The Campbells are coming*
D.6014, Old King Cole: *Old King Cole*

Air-tight Tobacco Jars

D.5844, Old Charley
D.5845, Paddy
Introduced 1938; withdrawn 1960

Sairey Gamp teapot

Jester and
Old Charley
wall vases

Teapots

D.6015, Sairey Gamp
D.6016, Tony Weller
D.6017, Old Charley
Introduced 1939; withdrawn 1960

Wall Vases

D.6110, Old Charley
D.6111, Jester (not to be confused with
wall masks of Jesters produced in 1934,
and included in the HN range)
Introduced 1940; withdrawn 1960

John Barleycorn   Parson Brown   Dick Turpin   Old Charley

Match-Stands and Ash Trays

D.5599, Old Charley
D.5600, Parson Brown
D.5601, Dick Turpin
D.5602, John Barleycorn
Introduced 1936; withdrawn 1960

Parson Brown   Auld Mac   Paddy

Ash Bowls

D.5925, Old Charley
D.5926, Paddy
Introduced 1938; withdrawn 1960
D.6006, Auld Mac
D.6007, Farmer John
D.6008, Parson Brown
D.6009, Sairey Gamp
Introduced 1939; withdrawn 1960

Old Charley   Farmer John   Sairey Gamp

Tony Weller   Mr Micawber   Sairey Gamp

Larger size bust of Sairey Gamp, from a set of four first produced in the HN series in 1934. The other subjects are Pickwick, Micawber and Tony Weller. They were originally sold mounted on a polished wooden base to be used as bookends.

Sam Weller   Buz Fuz   Mr Pickwick

Busts
D.6047, Sairey Gamp
D.6048, Buz Fuz
D.6049, Mr Pickwick
D.6050, Mr Micawber
D.6051, Tony Weller
D.6052, Sam Weller
Introduced 1939; withdrawn 1960

Paddy

Miniature Sugars
D.6150, Sairey Gamp
D.6151, Paddy
D.6152, Old Charley
Introduced 1940; withdrawn 1960
These are sometimes referred to as Toothpick Holders by American collectors

Sugar Bowls
D.6011, Sairey Gamp
D.6012, Old Charley
D.6013, Tony Weller
Introduced 1939; withdrawn 1960

Tony Weller

Napkin Rings

M.57 Mr Pickwick   M.60 Tony Weller
M.58 Mr Micawber   M.61 Sam Weller
M.59 Fat Boy   M.62 Sairey Gamp

The set of napkin rings were given M numbers for record purposes but these do not always appear on the ware. Some sets were produced in gift boxes. The rings were introduced in about 1939 and withdrawn in 1960

Mr Pickwick   Cap'n Cuttle   Buz Fuz   Mr Micawber

Table Cigarette Lighters

These lighters, now much-prized collectors' items, were made up from small-size Character Jugs fitted with a special lighting mechanism. They were marketed only in North America but as many perhaps as 200 were presented as gifts to friends of the Chairman of Doulton & Co. Limited so that they are occasionally found in the United Kingdom and elsewhere.

The following are the thirteen subjects which are officially known to have been adapted as lighters, with the dates of introduction and withdrawal. (Four subjects were in production for *one year only*).

Bacchus 1964–1973
Beefeater 1958–1973
Buz Fuz 1958 only
Captain Ahab 1964–1973

Cap'n Cuttle 1958 only
Falstaff 1958–1973
Lawyer 1962–1973
Long John Silver 1958–1973
Mr Micawber 1958 only
Mr Pickwick 1958–1961
Musketeer (Porthos) 1958 only
Old Charley 1959–1973
Poacher 1958–1973
Rip van Winkle 1958 only

Retail prices over the period 1958–1973 ranged from U.S. Dollars 13.50 to 20.00

Other subjects may have been piloted and collectors frequently refer to lighters adapted from other small size character jugs, for example *Granny*. No such lighter was ever produced by Doulton, but the reason why this and other subjects are reported from time to time may be as follows. Before Doulton began to manufacture lighters themselves there was a company in New York which produced lighters set into small-size jugs. This was done by filling the jugs with plaster of Paris and setting the cups that held the lighters into the plaster while it was still soft. When hard, the plaster was painted black and the lighter mechanisms inserted. Any small-size jug could have been adapted in this way.

Sometime in 1957 the New York company gave up manufacturing these lighters and Doulton began to produce the purpose-made jugs adapted so that there was just the hole open at the top to accommodate the lighter. The Doulton lighters can therefore easily be distinguished from the plaster models and from the ordinary small-size jugs.

Liqueur or Wine Containers
During the 1960s some small-size character jugs fitted with special stoppers were supplied to W. Walklate Limited, for use as liqueur or wine bottles. *The Poacher*, *Falstaff* and *Rip van Winkle* were adapted for this purpose, but there may have been others.

Rip van Winkle   Falstaff   Poacher

When the devil was sick
 the devil a saint would be
When the devil got well
 devil a saint was he

A Note on Dating

Some jugs and other items, as can be seen from the preceding lists, were in production for only a few years and can thus be dated fairly closely. The dating of jugs made over a long period (including, of course, some still being made) is much more difficult.

It has been stated in some articles in the press that the oldest Royal Doulton Character and Toby Jugs have a capital 'A' close to the usual Lion and Crown back-stamp. It has been assumed also that this 'A' was peculiar to these jugs. Neither of these assertions is correct.

The 'A' was simply a factory control mark to route wares to a particular kiln; similar wares made *at the same time* and intended to be routed to other kilns did not bear the 'A' mark.

The 'A' mark can be found on a variety of wares besides these jugs, including tablewares, Bunnykins nursery ware, vases, etc., bearing actual impressed dates or symbols indicating dates, ranging *between 1939 and 1955*. The 'A' alone, therefore, is not a very useful guide and does not *necessarily* indicate that the jug is a very early one.

On the basis of correspondence with dealers and collectors and the examination of specimen jugs, it seems likely that the oldest jugs are those which simply bear the words (in addition to the trade mark) 'Reg. applied for' or just one Registered Design Number (i.e. the English one).

Next came jugs with their names printed in double 'inverted commas'. These are found with and without the 'A' and with and without the Registered Number. It would seem that the factory until the late 1950s had no consistent method of marking and it was a matter of luck sometimes which particular mark or marks were applied. It would be a great boon to future collectors if all jugs – and indeed, all other wares – could bear the actual impressed or printed year of production or else a symbol indicating this. This used to be done in years gone by.

Since about 1950 most jugs have been marked under the normal Lion and Crown trade-mark with the printed name, D. number and *several* Registered Numbers (differing for various countries in which the design has been registered). However, some jugs introduced in the early 1950s carry only one Registered Number.

There was not room on the 'Tinies' to put the usual mark. Most of these bear just the name circumscribed by the words ROYAL DOULTON – MADE IN ENGLAND.

A Note on Handles

The handles on some of the earlier Character Jugs – for example *John Barleycorn*, *Old Charley*, *Parson Brown*, *Mephistopheles* and *Toby Philpot* – were quite ordinary and utilitarian.

For *Sairey Gamp* however, the modeller had the bright idea of shaping the handle as an umbrella. This practice of associating the form of the handle in some apt way with the character depicted by the jug was generally followed thereafter. Thus *Simon the Cellarer* has his bunch of keys, *John Peel* his hunting crop, the *Gondolier* has the prow of his gondola, the *Old Salt* his mermaid, and so on.

Discontinued Character and Toby Jugs

The following list gives the dates of introduction and withdrawal of *discontinued* jugs and is arranged in chronological order beginning with the first jug in the series, John Barleycorn, introduced in 1934.

Collectors will be able to see at once from this list how long each jug was in production. Broadly speaking, the shorter this period the more valuable the jug is likely to become. Of course, as time goes on, *all* discontinued jugs – even those which were in production for many years – will tend to become more and more difficult to find and collectors will do well to keep on the look-out for such jugs, including those most recently withdrawn. It will be noted that quite a number of jugs introduced since 1950 were withdrawn after only a few years.

The following abbreviations are used in this list: L (large), S (small), M (miniature) and T (tiny). The asterisk * indicates the six Dickens characters originally produced in a size c. $4\frac{1}{2}$ inches (11 cm) high, intermediate between the usual large and small sizes. The approximate dimensions of the various sizes are given on page 40.

John Barleycorn (L) 1934–60
Simon the Cellarer (L) 1935–60
Dick Turpin first version (L) 1935–60
Parson Brown (L and S) 1935–60
Touchstone (L) 1936–60
Simon the Cellarer (S) 1936–60
Cardinal (L) 1936–60
Dick Turpin, first version (S) 1936–60
Jester (S) 1936–60
John Peel (L) 1936–60
Tony Weller (L and S) 1936–60
Vicar of Bray (L) 1936–60
Clown, orange hair (L) 1937–c.1943
John Barleycorn (S) 1937–60
John Peel (S) 1937–60
Mephistopheles (L and S) 1937–48
Paddy (L and S) 1937–60
Toby Philpots (L and S) 1937–69
Buz Fuz (*) 1938–48
Cap'n Cuttle (*) 1938–48
Fat Boy (*) 1938–48
Mr Micawber (*) 1938–48
Mr Pickwick (*) 1938–48
Sam Weller (*) 1938–48
Farmer John (L and S) 1938–60
Cardinal (S) 1939–60
John Barleycorn (M) 1939–60
Old King Cole (L and S) 1939–60
Paddy (M) 1939–60
Toby Philpots (M) 1939–69
Tony Weller (M) 1939–60
Cardinal (M) 1940–60
Cavalier (L) 1940–60
Drake (L) 1940–60
Fat Boy (M and T) 1940–60
John Peel (M) 1940–60
Mr Micawber (M and T) 1940–60
Old Charley (T) 1940–60
Paddy (T) 1940–60
Mr Pickwick (L) 1940–60
Sairey Gamp (T) 1940–60

Sam Weller (L, M and T) 1940–60
Dick Turpin (M) 1940–60
Churchill (L) 1940–c.1942
Cavalier (S) 1941–60
Drake (S) 1941–60
Auld Mac (T) 1946–60
Smuts, Field-Marshal (L) 1946–48
'Arriet (L, S, M, and T) 1947–60
'Arry (L, S, M and T) 1947–60
Cardinal (T) 1947–60
John Peel (T) 1947–60
Mr Pickwick (M and T) 1947–60
Robin Hood, first version (L, S and M) 1947–60
Buz Fuz (S) 1948–60
Cap'n Cuttle (S) 1948–60
Fat Boy (S) 1948–60
Mr Micawber (S) 1948–60
Mr Pickwick (S) 1948–60
Sam Weller (S) 1948–60
Jarge (L and S) 1950–60
Samuel Johnson (L and S) 1950–60
Clown, white hair (L) 1951–55
Friar Tuck (L) 1951–60
Lord Nelson (L) 1952–69
Uncle Tom Cobbleigh (L) 1952–60
Dick Whittington (L) 1953–60
Johnny Appleseed (L) 1953–69
Simple Simon (L) 1953–60
Fortune Teller (L and S) 1959–67
Mikado (L and S) 1959–69
Viking (L and S) 1959–75
Fortune Teller (M) 1960–67
Mikado (M) 1960–69
Town Crier (L, S and M) 1960–73
Viking (M) 1960–75
Gladiator (L, S, and M) 1961–67
Gulliver (L, S, and M) 1962–67
Regency Beau (L, S and M) 1962–67
Scaramouche (L, S, and M) 1962–67
Gondolier (L, S, and M) 1964–69
Punch and Judy Man (L, S, and M) 1964–69
'Ard of 'Earing (L, S, and M) 1964–67
Capt. Hook (L, S, and M) 1965–71
Ugly Duchess (L, S, and M) 1965–73
St. George (L and S) 1968–75
Jockey (L) 1971–75

Discontinued Toby Jugs
The Best is Not Too Good: 1939–60
Cap'n Cuttle: 1948–60
Charrington Toby
Cliff Cornell
Double XX: 1939–69
The Fat Boy: 1948–60
George Robey
Mr Micawber: 1948–60
Mr Pickwick: 1948–60
Old Charley: 1939–69
Sairey Gamp: 1948–60
Sam Weller: 1948–60
The Squire: 1950–69

All the above, except the Cliff Cornell jugs, were made in one size only

Appendix

Introductions for 1980

The following new Character Jugs
will be introduced during 1980

Anne of Cleeves

Designer: M. Abberley
The fourth wife of Henry VIII, and
the fifth in the Character Jug series

Mark Twain

Designer: E. J. Griffiths
The popular American author,
forever associated with Huckleberry
Finn

Ann Boleyn

Small and miniature

Lobster Man

Miniature